MW00588625

Praise for Sur

'It is difficult to over
concise, convincingly argued view of our world's prospects
for its survival and improvement.' *Books + Publishing*

Praise for Tim Flannery and *The Weather Makers*

'At last, here is a clear and readable account of one of the most
important but controversial issues facing everyone in the world
today. If you are not already addicted to Tim Flannery's writing,
discover him now: this is his best book yet.' Jared Diamond

'It would be hard to imagine a better or more
important book.' Bill Bryson

'This is the book the world has been waiting for—and needing—
for decades. At last, a book that sets out, for the general public,
the irrefutable evidence that climate change is already happening,
and we need to become very serious about it—fast.' Peter Singer

'This is a magnificent book; exciting, poetic, passionate—and
full of knowledge we all need and can act upon before it's too late.'
Redmond O'Hanlon

'Like Jared Diamond and Stephen Jay Gould, Tim Flannery
has the ability to take complex ideas and—seemingly effortlessly—
make them accessible. This book captures your imagination
through its extraordinary range of argument, its vivid imagery,
its wealth of research, quick wit and richness of detail.'
Sydney Morning Herald

'With his effortless storytelling and breath-taking
research, Tim Flannery makes the issue of climate change
completely accessible.' *Victorian Lifestyle*

'This man is a national treasure, and we should heed his
every word.' *Sunday Telegraph*

Also by Tim Flannery

Mammals of New Guinea

Tree Kangaroos: A Curious Natural History with R. Martin, P. Schouten and A. Szalay

The Future Eaters

Possums of the World: a Monograph of the Phalangeroidea with P. Schouten

Mammals of the South West Pacific and Moluccan Islands

Watkin Tench, *1788* (ed.)

John Nicol, *Life and Adventures 1776–1801* (ed.)

Throwim Way Leg: An Adventure

The Explorers (ed.)

The Birth of Sydney (ed.)

Terra Australis: Matthew Flinders' Great Adventures in the Circumnavigation of Australia (ed.)

The Eternal Frontier

A Gap in Nature with P. Schouten

John Morgan, *The Life and Adventures of William Buckley* (ed.)

The Birth of Melbourne (ed.)

Joshua Slocum, *Sailing Alone around the World* (ed.)

Astonishing Animals with P. Schouten

Country

The Weather Makers

We Are the Weather Makers

An Explorer's Notebook

Here on Earth

Among the Islands

The Mystery of the Venus Island Fetish

Atmosphere of Hope

Tim Flannery is a leading writer on climate change. Scientist, explorer and conservationist, he has held various academic positions including Professor at the University of Adelaide, Director of the South Australian Museum, Principal Research Scientist at the Australian Museum, Professorial Fellow at the Melbourne Sustainable Society Institute, University of Melbourne, and Panasonic Professor of Environmental Sustainability, Macquarie University. His books include the award-winning international bestseller *The Weather Makers, Here on Earth* and *Atmosphere of Hope.* Flannery was the 2007 Australian of the Year. He is currently Chief Councillor of the Climate Council.

TIM FLANNERY

SUNLIGHT
AND
SEAWEED

An Argument for How to Feed, Power and Clean Up the World

TEXT PUBLISHING MELBOURNE AUSTRALIA

textpublishing.com.au

The Text Publishing Company
Swann House
22 William Street
Melbourne Victoria 3000
Australia

First published by The Text Publishing Company 2017
Reprinted 2017 (twice)

Book design by Jessica Horrocks
Cover photograph by Javier Pardina/Stocksy
Typeset by J&M Typesetters

Printed in Australia by Griffin Press, an Accredited ISO AS/NZS 14001:2004
Environmental Management System printer.

National Library of Australia Cataloguing-in-Publication
Creator: Flannery, Tim F. (Tim Fridtjof), 1956– author.
Title: Sunlight and seaweed : an argument for how to feed, power and clean
up the world.
ISBN: 9781925498684 (paperback)
ISBN: 9781925410907 (ebook)
Subjects: Sustainable living. Sustainable development. Sustainable agricul-
ture. Renewable energy resources. Social change—Environmental aspects.
Nature—Effect of human beings on. Population—Environmental aspects.
Pollution. Climate changes—Technological innovations.

This book is printed on paper certified against the Forest
Stewardship Council® Standards. Griffin Press holds FSC
chain-of-custody certification SGS-COC-005088. FSC promotes
environmentally responsible, socially beneficial and economically
viable management of the world's forests.

To three of my inspirations,
CH, KH and MM

Contents

Introduction

There is no doubt that humanity is nearing a crisis point. Old ways of doing things, from growing food to providing energy and manufacturing the countless things we feel we need, have proved to be so damaging to human health and the environment that within a few decades they must be no more. Entirely new methods of providing life's essentials must be devised to take their place. And, indeed, those alternatives are beginning to take shape. But will they arrive in time? In a nutshell, *that*—along with the pressing need to revitalise our democracies—is our challenge.

Some believe that by living simple lives—growing our food at home, generating electricity from solar panels on our rooftops, and living with less in terms of material goods—we will be able to live sustainably in future. There are doubtless great virtues in simple living, but the world's population stands at 7.4 billion and is rapidly growing. Billions are only now attaining modest affluence, and soon will aspire keenly to the lifestyles of those in the richest nations. I believe that even with the best intentions, unless new technologies capable of providing life's essentials cleanly and cheaply arrive soon, we cannot live sustainably. In fact, the situation is worse than that, because without new technologies and new ways of doing things, we will not be able to deal with the climate crisis and the land, air and sea pollution that so afflicts our world.

Some believe that we already have the technologies we need to do this, and looking at the rapidity with which solar panels are colonising the world's rooftops, it is indeed easy to be misled into believing that the clean technology revolution is well underway, and that there is little need for innovative new solutions. In truth, the clean energy revolution has barely started. As of mid-2015, solar photovoltaics was contributing just 1 per cent of global electricity.[1] As important a breakthrough as it was, solar PV is best thought of as just the earliest development in a highly complex energy revolution that will unfold over decades and will end, perhaps, by transforming our species into a new breed of alchemists, capable of satisfying our needs out of little more than sunlight and thin air. In this context, the spread of solar PV is analogous to the spread of Alexander Graham Bell's telephone: ultimately, telephone wires would enable the internet. But for most of the time that land-line telephones have been in existence, nobody was thinking about them in relation to the next big step.

The three objectives of feeding, powering and cleaning up the world may seem to have little in common, and it may seem to be overly ambitious to suggest solutions to these enormous problems in a book as brief as this. But I am not attempting to present complete solutions here. Instead, what I want to do is to point out common solutions, which already exist in embryo, and which have the potential to underpin the achievement of all three of these essential prerequisites for a sustainable future.

Much of my recent writing spelled out a message of hope for the future. It is clear to me that even with the climate crisis assuming its current frightening proportions, and with billions more people on our finite planet, that life in 2050 can be much better than it is today, and the state of our biodiversity and ecosystems much improved. But as I have watched recent developments I have realised hope is not enough. We also need a coherent vision of the future that is capable of guiding investments in clean technologies so that hope can be turned into concrete reality. This book outlines the possible roles that multi-potent solutions can play in addressing humanity's greatest environmental challenges. But in order to examine potential solutions and how they might work, the full scale and nature of our sustainability crisis must be understood.

The Paris Agreement on climate change, which

was concluded in December 2015, heralds renewed and, for the first time, globally coordinated efforts to address one of our most pressing pollution challenges—that of excess carbon in the atmosphere. Although belated, the agreement will see a reduction in the burning of fossil fuels and an acceleration of the move towards clean energy. It's a great starting point, but little more. The concentration of atmospheric greenhouse gases and the warming it is driving are already dangerously high. As I have argued previously in *Atmosphere of Hope*, if we are to solve the climate problem we must not only generate energy cleanly, but draw carbon pollution from the atmosphere—an imperative increasingly supported by both scientists and policy makers.[2] 'Third-way' technologies, such as kelp farming or direct air capture of CO_2, aim to remove atmospheric carbon by mimicking or strengthening Earth's systems for regulating the carbon cycle. But, sadly, third-way technologies are far less advanced than clean-energy technologies, and the technological and economic obstacles, as well as the scale of the actions required, remain formidable.

But even these climate-related challenges, as large as they are, are not the only sustainability issues that require urgent attention. By 2050 there will be about 9 billion people sharing our finite planet. Despite some progress, the challenge of limiting population growth remains. And the task of simply feeding the ever-growing multitude is as difficult as any challenge faced by our species. Then there is the problem of cleaning up the innumerable pollutants, quite aside from CO_2, that contaminate our air, water and soil, and which result from centuries of unsustainable mining, industry and agriculture. Cumulatively, these challenges are growing more daunting by the year. They are perhaps best summed up in WWF's Living Planet report, which reveals that we are already using 50 per cent more resources than Earth can sustainably yield, and that as we do so, we are destroying Earth's natural capital and so compromising our planet's ability to provide the clean air, water, food and other ecosystem services that life depends upon.[3]

Just how the consequences of our overconsumption of Earth's resources (including its ability to deal with pollution) may play out over the next 40 years has been examined in detail recently by Dr Jørgen Randers. Randers was a co-author of the Club of Rome's influential book *The Limits to Growth*. In 2012, on the 40th anniversary of the publication of that work, he undertook a new study. Titled *2052: A Global Forecast for the Next Forty Years*, it is based on a very different method of analysis from that which underpinned his earlier book.[4] Instead of developing complex scenarios, he asked his friends (who happen to be the leaders in various fields relating to sustainability) what they thought. The result is, I believe, the most convincing account of the future ever written, and its message is even more urgent and compelling than that of *The Limits to Growth*. Randers sees the world in 2052 as bleak, a result largely of incremental rather than abrupt change. He thinks that the effort required to lift billions out of poverty will be so great that it will force a reliance on fossil fuels for far longer than is wise. By 2052, he thinks, we will be looking back on forty years of accelerating climate impacts, and bracing ourselves for imminent runaway climate change. This, he anticipates, will finally force unified action to clean up our energy- and food-production systems. But the cost of the preceding inaction will be very high. Overcoming decades of inequality, tension and social strife will cause some nations to collapse. Longevity will not continue to increase as it has over recent generations and may even decline. For all but the wealthiest of the current elites living in the affluent west, a decline in living standards will be so precipitous that it will feel like a collapse.

Randers' pathway to 2052 is a messy, muddle-through kind of route to the future that we should not wish on our children. And I feel certain that we can avoid it, in part through the swift deployment of new technologies. But that will take vision and leadership, and some luck.

This book focusses on two solutions that I think must be a big part of humanity's future if we are to avoid Randers' 2052 vision. Neither one is a complete solution to every sustainability problem we face. Rather, they are fundamental building blocks towards solutions to multiple problems. Technologies or methods that solve more than one problem at once are required if we are to rise to the multiplicity of challenges facing us, as energy, food production and environmental remediation are interrelated and, indeed, synergistic undertakings. The first, known as Concentrated Solar Thermal (CST), is capable of delivering an energy trifecta—electricity, high-quality heat and energy storage, as well as clean water. CST will play a vital role in limiting greenhouse gas emissions, in growing food sustainably at a very large scale and in cleaning up polluted soils and water—potentially all at the same time. The second, PV-powered mid-ocean kelp farming (PMKF)—which strictly speaking is a method rather than a technology (although it does have unique technological dimensions)—stands out for its enormous potential to capture and sequester carbon from the air and ocean, while yielding prodigious volumes of high-quality protein.

Armed with CST and PMKF, humanity will command cheap, clean power harnessed to the most efficient food-production systems yet devised, which, as they work, have the potential to clean up the environment on a massive scale. Of all the energy and food solutions to date, I argue that only CST and PMKF can deliver this. Although neither is entirely new, emerging developments promise to transform CST from a struggling field of energy generation into one of the most important technologies for humanity's future, as well as to kick-start PMKF at a massive scale. In short, I believe that we are moving into a solar-thermal, kelp-powered future. But will it come fast enough?

CHAPTER 1

The Population Bomb

In 1968, Stanford University's Professor Paul Ehrlich and his wife Anne wrote one of the most influential and hotly debated books of the twentieth century. *The Population Bomb* sold more than two million copies and had a profound effect on a generation.[1] Even today, nearly 50 years after its first publication, whenever I speak about environmental matters I'm sure to get at least one question about population, often accompanied by a mention of the Ehrlichs' book.

The Population Bomb warned urgently of the dangers of runaway population growth. In it, the

Ehrlichs noted that global population had doubled since 1930 and was set to double again. We now know that this predicted doubling will occur before 2030. At the time the book was written, there was no end of such rapid population growth in sight. The Club of Rome was established in the year of the book's publication, and its warnings about the perils of humanity's then-current path, published in *The Limits to Growth* in 1972, reinforced the fears of many—that unless it was stopped, our rapid population growth could only end in disaster.

In *The Population Bomb*, the Ehrlichs controversially claimed that mass starvation would kill hundreds of millions of people during the 1970s and 80s. For some, the claim brought visions of famines similar to Ireland's horrific potato famine of the 1840s. Such stark events did not occur, which led many who did not like the book's message to deride both it and its authors. But the Ehrlichs were not wrong. Many millions of people did die from malnutrition and hunger during the 1980s and 90s. And they continue to die from these preventable causes today. But that is only one dimension of a complex story. For, despite the terrible toll of malnourishment, since *The Population Bomb* was written, humans have managed to increase the food production per head of population. Indeed, in the early 1990s one expert on food security wrote:

> The world food situation has never appeared better. Enough food is being produced today that, if it were evenly distributed, no one should have to go hungry.[2]

As far as food per capita goes, in the decades since the 1990s the situation has improved substantially. By 2007, nearly enough food was being consumed to adequately feed the entire human population. But because some of that food was being fed to animals, and because some of us consume more than our fair share, 2.5 billion people live in countries with inadequate per-capita food supplies. As a result, around a billion people continue to suffer from hunger.[3]

Despite progress to date, the challenges remain enormous. Taking into account population growth and shifting dietary preferences, humanity will need to produce 69 per cent more food energy in 2050 than we did in 2006.[4] The challenge of providing this is made far more daunting by the unsustainable nature of most of our current agricultural practices. By one estimate, agriculture currently produces 24 per cent of all human-caused greenhouse gases, uses the most productive 37 per cent of the land surface, and accounts for 70 per cent of all the fresh water used by people.[5] There is clearly no way of getting the current system to provide 69 per cent more kilojoules—there just isn't enough land, water or room for carbon in our skies to do that. Instead, agriculture in the future will need to be quite different from the agriculture of today, and one of the things that will determine how rapid and extensive that change must be is our ever-increasing demand, which is driven in large part by our rate of population growth, and compounded by overconsumption, misleading advertising and corporate malfeasance. Thankfully, one of the things that has changed in the last 40 years is that vista, conjured so ably by the Ehrlichs, of endless, rapid human population growth.

We have a far clearer picture today than the Ehrlichs had in 1968 of the great demographic trends shaping human destiny. The end of population growth is now arguably in sight. The Population Division of the United Nations Department of Economic and Social Affairs closely monitors global population growth. Its projections have proved highly accurate. Their latest report notes that in 2015 the human population stood at 7.3 billion (other sources estimated it at 7.5 billion in early 2017),[6] and that it was almost certain that it would reach around 8.5 billion by 2030.[7]

Human demographic trends are highly predictable over a period of a few decades. That's because, like the *Titanic*, they have great inertia: it takes the efforts of generations to alter the trajectory of a large population. The most significant uncertainty in the UN's projection concerns the few countries with very high population growth rates, such as Nigeria and Pakistan. Because these countries have such a high proportion of the population in the child-bearing age range, increases or decreases in family size there can have a relatively large impact on the global trend. But, even so, some experts believe that the numbers will only vary by 100 million or so on either side of the 8.5 billion estimate.[8]

The importance of the high-fertility-rate countries to future population growth underlines a very important fact. If you are concerned about unsustainable population growth, you can do something about it by increasing the economic status and access to fertility control of women in the poorest countries. It is axiomatic that improvements in the economic and social status of women of childbearing age results in a lower birthrate. As childhood mortality drops, women gain confidence that their children will survive, which also results in a drop in the birthrate. Movements from the countryside to the city also help. On a farm, children provide extra labour. But in the city, where both parents often work away from the home, childcare and education are required if offspring are to contribute economically to the family in the long term. Education is expensive in developing countries, so in cities in the developing world parents tend to have just one or two children. Almost all of the 40 countries with birthrates above four are in sub-Saharan Africa, with notable exceptions being war-racked states like Afghanistan and Pakistan.[9] Focussing our charitable and foreign aid efforts in such places, particularly on initiatives that benefit and empower women of childbearing age, will do more to limit global population and improve the quality of lives than any other investment we can make.

There are some very interesting aspects to the population story that are not fully captured by the bald global figures, yet which are crucial to a full understanding of our population future. The total human fertility rate (TFR) is a projection (rather than an actual count) of the total number of children women in their childbearing years are likely to bear. Another way of thinking about the TFR is that it embodies the fertility of a single, imaginary woman, who during her reproductive life is subject to all of the annual fertility rates she passes through between ages 15 to 49. For women who are still of childbearing age, of course, the TFR cannot be an actual statistic, for their childbearing years are not over. Despite being a projection, the TFR is important because it gives a far clearer picture of global fertility than the birthrate. This is because it is not influenced by population 'bulges' such as the baby boomer generation, where birthrates are temporarily high.

The TFR is not, however, entirely reliable as a predictor of future trends if large numbers of women defer birth until later in their life—a trend, incidentally, which is increasingly seen in developed countries like the UK, where, for example, in 2016 the number of babies born to women over 40 in England and Wales exceeded those born to women under 20—the first time this had happened since 1947.[10]

There is an even more accurate measure of human fertility than the TFR. Known as the net reproductive rate (NRR), it predicts the number of daughters which that same imaginary woman embodied in the TFR would have over her lifetime. This is a superior measure because, from a population perspective, the number of men in a population is pretty much irrelevant to the birthrate (as long as there are enough to father the children): it is the number of women who influence the total fertility. Unfortunately, the UN stopped measuring the NRR in 1998. But as we shall soon see, it is of increasing relevance. In light of the absence of UN data on the NRR, for the purposes of the current discussion we must return to the TFR, which plays a major role in UN population analyses.

In the half-decade beginning 1950, the TFR was nearly 5 (4.95), and in the half-decade during which the Ehrlichs wrote *The Population Bomb* it had barely dropped (to 4.85). Hence, the deep concern during the 1960s about population growth. But by the half-decade starting 2010, the TFR had fallen to just 2.36. In other words, over 50 years the TFR had more than halved. This is an astonishing change, and the reasons behind it represent one of the best hopes for our future.

You might have assumed that a TFR sufficient to replace the population would be 2 (enough to replace the mother and father). But this is not the case. Because some women die before reaching their reproductive years (especially in developing countries), the replacement figure is in fact 2.33. Thus, the current TFR only needs to drop by 0.03 per cent to come down to the replacement level. At that point, unless there is a reversal, the human population will trend towards zero growth. And it seems very likely that the TFR will indeed drop to 2.33 during the half-decade beginning 2020. Which is, at most, just eight years away.

A population that is trending towards zero growth because it has reached replacement has not necessarily stopped growing. It can continue to grow for a while because, for example, some age groups are larger than others (population 'bulges'). The baby-boomer generation experienced in developed countries following the Second World War is an example of this. In addition, populations with replacement birthrates can continue to grow because people live longer. We are seeing both trends play out in the early twenty-first century, so population continues to grow at the rate of around 75 million per year. Yet we will soon still be on a curve towards zero growth.[11]

Reaching a replacement level TFR will be momentous. If it does indeed occur in the first five years of the 2020s, humanity as a whole will have gone through the demographic transition—from a high-birthrate and high-death-rate population, to a low-birth- and death-rate population—in little more than a century. This is an astonishing fact, which speaks eloquently of the global interconnectedness of our lives and cultures. It also marks out humanity as something special, for we are the only species in the entire history of life which appears to be on track to self-regulate our population, the populations of all other species being regulated by external factors such as food availability, disease and predators.

The problem of population growth increasing exponentially, while food supply increases only linearly, was first elucidated by Thomas Malthus in 1798.[12] The logic of what has become known as the Malthusian paradigm is so persuasive that it has influenced social, economic and scientific thinking ever since. And it applies with a terrible inevitability to every species we share our planet with. To learn that it does not apply to our human species after all—because we look set to self-limit our population, rather than having nature do it for us in the form of starvation, predation or disease—is enormously liberating and a source of great hope and wonderment.

The methods of analysis used by the demographers at the UN are not the only ones that can be useful in examining humanity's population future. The highly respected Austrian-based International Institute for Applied Systems Analysis (IIASA) uses a very different model to predict the future population. In addition to briefings from in-country experts, they factor in education levels, which influence family size profoundly. Interestingly, their most likely projection is for a population of 9.4 billion by

2070, with a decline to below 9 billion by 2100.[13]

Using a holistic assessment of a range of trends, as assessed by experts, including climate impacts, and macro-economic, social and technological developments, Jørgen Randers sees human population reaching a maximum of only 8.1 billion by the early 2040s, and declining thereafter with accelerating speed.[14] One of the most important drivers of this outcome is, Randers states, plummeting birthrates brought about in large part by mass migration from farms to cities. Strikingly, Randers thinks that another brake on population growth will come from changes in the death rate. Mortality rates, he says, will rise from the 2030s onwards as a result of faltering economies and increasingly severe climate change, so increasing longevity will cease driving population up at the rate it currently is.

Randers' approach to projecting future demographic trends is, it must be admitted, unique. Moreover, his projections are outliers: most demographers anticipate a larger human population by 2050, and a much later population peak. According to its 2015 projection, for example, the UN expects the world population to reach 11.2 billion by 2100.[15] And according to a paper published in *Science*, the human population is likely to continue to grow well into the twenty-second century, and there's an 80 per cent probability that the human population will reach between 9.6 and 12.3 billion by 2100.[16] If the higher end of this projection proves correct, the problem of feeding the world will be far more acute than many had thought.

There are, of course, many factors that influence when population peaks and how rapidly it declines thereafter. One concerns the rate at which the world's poorest can gain access to contraception. And in this area there is some very good news. More than 30 million women in the world's poorest countries gained access to contraception between 2012 and 2015, well ahead of the historical trend of contraception uptake.[17] If the rate of uptake continues, and the remaining 225 million women who cannot access contraception might have the opportunity soon, the total human population at peak could be reduced by a billion.[18]

Another factor whose impact h: begun to feature significantly in : development of ultrasound techn 1980s. The human sex ratio at birth is 1.00 males for every female. The excess of males is offset by higher mortality rates at almost every age for men. And because women tend to live longer than men, the sex ratio for the total population tends to favour women over men. Until about 1990, in China, the world's most populous country, a roughly normal sex ratio prevailed. But soon thereafter things began to change. By 2005, the sex ratio among two year olds had reached 1.24.[19] The principal cause of the preponderance of male births is clear. Improved economic conditions, easy availability of ultrasound and relaxed attitudes towards the termination of pregnancy even at a late stage, along with the traditional preference for boy babies over girls, provide both the motive and the means.

The selective abortion of female foetuses whose gender was detected using ultrasound was the predominant factor in the sex ratio, but poor care of female infants is also contributing by reversing the normal postnatal mortality pattern. In other words, the welfare of some female infants is neglected to the point that it leads to a higher death rate than that of male infants. This may occur for reasons as simple as decisions about when to take a sick child to a doctor.

The situation these combined factors have created is not only tragic for individuals, but for China as a whole. For every 100 women in the age cohort born between 2003 and 2005 in China, there will be about 24 excess men. This astonishingly large imbalance between the sexes is bound to have profound implications for society as a whole. It must, among other things, change expectations in regard to marriage and sharply lower the country's future net reproductive rate (NRR). Unfortunately, the situation is not resolving quickly. In 2009 the sex ratio for newborns in China was 119.45, and by 2013 it had declined only slightly to 117.7.[20] For an entire generation and perhaps beyond, there will be a massive oversupply of men. Because longevity is increasing rapidly in China (it's currently about 75 years for women and 74 for men), the situation is likely to characterise most of the twenty-first century.

The world's second most-populous country, India, seems to be following China in its bias towards males. In 2011 the sex ratio in the 0 to 5 age range was 1.088. The great majority of Indians continue to live in rural areas, where economic circumstances are well below those in China, but the fact that sex ratios are higher among more affluent urban Indians than they are among poorer rural ones suggests that as economic conditions improve, India's sex ratio is likely to worsen.[21]

India and China are not alone in their growing preponderance of males. Today the world's highest sex ratios are found in the countries of the Caucasus region, which includes both Orthodox Christian and Muslim communities. There, the sex ratio ranges between 1.11 and 1.20. The additional males in this instance are largely the third born in a family. This suggests that families who have already had a boy and girl, or two girls, may use scanning technology and pregnancy termination to ensure that their third born is a son.[22]

The implications of high sex ratios in favour of males in the world's most populous nations, as well as several smaller ones, must have implications for our global future. Some commentators fear that sexual frustration and large numbers of males without immediate family ties represents a ticking social time bomb that will explode in violence and possibly war. Doubtless it is a highly undesirable situation. But, as seen in many societies in the past facing unusual circumstances in terms of sex ratios, humans have proved to be highly flexible in coping with the difficulties. Polyandry (where one wife has several husbands) is practised in at least four traditional societies in Tibet, Nepal, northern India and Western China. Elsewhere, large numbers of males and females live in single-sex monasteries and convents. Where there has been a shortage of men, such as in Germany after the world wars, the number of single mothers rose markedly. Of course we must seek to address the iniquitous social factors that perpetuate the oversupply of males over females. Simple humanity demands that. But the most sensible approach to the issue of the existing unbalanced sex ratios is that we should be aware of the problem, but maintain hope that solutions can be found for those who face a great personal difficulty in forming traditional family relationships.

Ultimately, biased sex ratios result from an undervaluing of women, and the disadvantage women suffer, even if they survive infancy, is often life-long. This is a human tragedy, as are the crushed hopes for a family life that many Chinese men face. Despite the undesirability of the situation, the demographic impacts of biased sex ratios are clear and unavoidable. As we have seen, the net reproductive rate (NRR) is the most influential measure of how rapidly a population will decline from its peak. I think that the low NRR (brought about by fewer women of reproductive age) in the world's largest countries, compounded by humanity's sharply declining total fertility rate (TFR) adds weight to the possibility that Randers is correct and that the global population will peak earlier than projected by the UN, and decline more sharply than expected.

CHAPTER 2

The State of the Planet

Whatever progress the ever-expanding mass of humanity has made to date in terms of bettering its circumstances, it has come at enormous environmental cost. One measure of that cost is our species 'ecological footprint', a concept pioneered by WWF. An ecological footprint of 1.0 represents humanity utilising precisely the maximum amount of resources that the planet could sustainably yield. Alarmingly, WWF's Global Footprint Network estimates that humanity's current footprint is around 1.5. That means that we're using 50 per cent more resources than our planet can sustainably provide. The lion's share of this footprint—in fact around half—results from our demand for energy derived from the burning of fossil fuels, which, in turn, results in the highly damaging and unsustainable emissions of greenhouse gases that are altering Earth's climate.[1] This is why those concerned about sustainability have been so focussed on solutions to the climate crisis. But as we address climate change, we must not forget the other stressors to Earth's ecosystems that comprise the other half of our ecological footprint. And one of the largest of those stressors results from our seemingly insatiable demand for fresh water.

We are quite literally draining dry some of Earth's greatest rivers and most expansive aquifers. Today, 2.7 billion people live in water catchments that, as a result of unsustainable extraction and population growth, experience severe water shortages for at least one month per year. With humanity taking so much of this essential element, other species are inevitably suffering. Indeed, of all Earth's ecosystems, its freshwater lakes, rivers and streams are the most environmentally stressed. Given the deteriorating state of the rainforests and coral reefs, that is quite a statement.[2]

One measure of the stress these ecosystems face is the dire state of aquatic vertebrate species. Globally, populations have fallen by half in just 40 years, and some species have been lost forever. China's greatest river, the Yangtze, is the third longest river on Earth, and, flowing through a region that has experienced unprecedented industrialisation, it has borne the brunt of the losses. Among the species to become extinct over the past decade are the iconic baiji dolphin, one of only four freshwater dolphin species on Earth, and the Chinese paddlefish.

The baiji was known as 'the goddess of the river' because Chinese fishermen believed that it endowed them with protection against natural disasters. The last sighting was in 2007, and it is now almost certainly extinct. Astonishingly, given the exploitation of whales over the past century, the baiji is the first member of the whale and dolphin family to be driven to extinction by human activities.

The loss of the Chinese paddlefish is at least as

great a catastrophe as the loss of the baiji. At up to seven metres long, it was among the largest fresh-water fish on the planet. A member of an exceedingly ancient family of fishes whose history extends back at least 300 million years, the last known individual was netted by illegal fishermen in the Yangtze River on 8 January 2007. The fish was a whopping 3.6 metres long and weighed 250 kilograms. Attempts were made to save it, but it had suffered fatal injuries while thrashing in the net. With the demise of the Chinese paddlefish, only one other member of the paddlefish family survives: the smaller American paddlefish, which inhabits the Mississippi River catchment, is becoming increasingly endangered through human activities and has already vanished from much of its historic distribution.

As sad as they are, the loss of these iconic species is merely the tip of a huge iceberg of environmental catastrophe. Prior to the extinction of the baiji and the Chinese paddlefish, Chinese experts had warned that 'reckless overfishing', the construction of dams, pollution and damaging land use had devastated fish stocks and biodiversity in the middle Yangtze.[3] Even in Europe, which has taken significant actions in recent decades to protect its waterways, more than a third of freshwater fish are threatened with extinction.[4] The situation is no better in North America. The continent is home to more than a third of the world's freshwater mussel species, but of the 302 documented species, 70 per cent are either extinct or in extreme danger of extinction.[5]

The state of Earth's rainforests also reflect our oversized ecological footprint. By 2000 about 50 per cent of the world's tropical rainforests that existed in 1800 had been destroyed. According to the UN's Food and Agriculture Organisation (FAO), in a rare bit of good news, the destruction of forests overall has slowed in the twenty-first century, with the rate of loss in 2015 being 50 per cent below what it was in 1990.[6] Rainforests, however, continue to be lost—by some estimates at a rate 8.5 per cent greater at the beginning of the twenty-first century than a decade earlier. By 2009, about 32,000 hectares were being lost each day. This destruction can wipe out entire ats, and scientists estimate that it is nction of about 135 plant and animal species per day, or 50,000 per year.[7]

Another useful measure of the oversized human ecological footprint—and particularly the half of it that does not relate directly to climate change, is the overall rate of species extinction during the twentieth century. The more severe impacts of climate change were only just beginning to be felt towards the end of the twentieth century, but other human activities were already profoundly modifying Earth's ecosystems and resulting in widespread extinctions. It has recently been demonstrated that the extinction rate for the twentieth century, when climate impacts were still small, was in fact 100 times higher than it would have been without human actions.[8] That rate is plainly unsustainable and a clear indicator of our current destructive path.

During the opening years of the twenty-first century however, with climate change impacts sharply increasing, the rate of extinction is set to get much worse. The severity of the problem was highlighted in the first half of 2016, when a strong El Niño spiked global surface temperatures to about 1.2°C above the preindustrial average. Prior to the El Niño, temperatures had climbed to about 0.9°C above the average, so the increase driven by the El Niño was around a third of a degree. The abrupt warming had a severe impact globally, but nowhere more so than on the world's coral reefs. A major coral bleaching event manifested globally, followed by severe coral mortality. The northern section of Australia's Great Barrier Reef was among the areas affected, and close monitoring there has permitted the full extent of the catastrophe to be documented. Surveys revealed that 93 per cent of all reefs that make up the northern section of the Great Barrier Reef suffered bleaching. By the end of the heatwave, 22 per cent of the reef's living coral was dead. Half of the Great Barrier Reef had already died by 2012, so today, only around a third of the corals that flourished on this magnificent structure a century ago survive.

I saw the damage caused by the most recent

bleaching first-hand in late May 2016, when I visited Opal Reef northeast of Port Douglas. The reef stands on the outer edge of the barrier, and because of its proximity to deep, cooler water, it had escaped previous bleaching episodes. But in 2016 it was in the frontline of a massive underwater heatwave that rolled in from the western Pacific. By the time I visited, the warmer water had killed about 90 per cent of the reef's delicate staghorn and plate corals and had damaged even some of the hardier massive corals. The abundant reef fish, particularly those which feed on live coral, were starving.

Just why underwater heatwaves are so damaging is due in part to the difficulty marine creatures have in shedding excess heat. They cannot sweat or wet their skin in other ways to cool themselves by transpiration, as land-based organisms can. Unless they are mobile and can move to cooler waters, they must simply put up with the heat. Even near-shore communities can be severely affected. As the Great Barrier Reef was bleaching, hundreds of hectares of mangrove forests were being killed by the heat and lack of rain in the Gulf of Carpentaria.[9] Added to the problems aquatic organisms face in shedding heat is the scarcity of oxygen in warm water. As one-fifth of the Great Barrier Reef died in 2016, mass fish kills occurred in the waters off northwestern Australia, presumably due to lack of oxygen, while on the reef itself, barramundi and other large fish were impossible to catch. They sat inactive and not feeding, in deep, potentially cooler areas where they had a chance of survival until the heatwave passed.

Recovery from such extreme damage as that which occurred on Opal Reef in May 2016 is theoretically possible, but it takes a long time. Bleaching of corals was still going on in the northern sector of the reef in July—mid-winter on the Great Barrier Reef, and in March 2017 bleaching was again detected—it is the first time ever that two consecutive years of coral bleaching have occurred.[10] After the corals die, algae grows on the dead coral structures. During episodes of rough weather, the dead corals break down, and a dense growth of algae covers the coral rubble, preventing coral recolonisation. Things can

for years, until eventually a cyclone
rubble and algae away, creating the
opportunity for recolonisation. But that requires the
survival of healthy parent corals nearby. And, of
course, new corals start life small. It takes several
decades for a diverse reef of large adult corals to
become re-established. Sadly, in light of Earth's ever-
rising average temperatures, there is little chance
that the long recovery process will ever be completed
over much of the Great Barrier Reef. Indeed, by the
2030s, the extreme conditions seen in 2016 will be
the new normal. In effect, through our addiction to
fossil fuels, we have probably already sealed the fate
of these exquisitely beautiful, diverse and complex
marvels.

It is striking that the impacts of the warming on
places like Opal Reef had not been foreseen as imminent by scientists. Most had expected the southern
section of the reef to suffer sooner and more severely
than the northern section. Previous bleaching events
had been driven by warm water accumulating over
the reef lagoon, and had greater effect on near-shore

and southern stretches of coral. The surprise destruction of the northern Great Barrier Reef serves to remind us that the future impacts of climate change on biodiversity are likely to be as unexpected as they are devastating.

The long-term warming trend is having other, compounding impacts on the reef's biodiversity. In mid-2016, scientists announced the first mammal extinction as a direct result of climate change. The Bramble Cay melomys was a medium-sized rodent that was unique to a small coral kay in the Great Barrier Reef. It had become extinct by 2014 when rising seas caused by global warming destroyed its habitat.[11] Rising seas and altered currents are also endangering turtle nesting sites. Raine Island on the Great Barrier Reef is the world's largest green turtle nesting site. But rising oceans have seen hatchling success rates plummet.[12] Right across northern Australia, the ecosystems that have long predominated are slipping away and being replaced with ecosystems that are far less diverse, productive and beautiful.

As dire as the destruction of the coral reefs and their ecosystems is, scientists warn of further, cascading climate impacts as our oceans heat and acidify. With 1.5°C of warming all but locked in by the existing burden of greenhouse gases in the atmosphere, there are compelling reasons to shift away from fossil fuels and so reduce our oversized ecological footprint. Thankfully, that shift has now begun in a way that seems to be irreversible.

CHAPTER 3

Eclipse: The Twilight of Fossil Fuels

The speed at which we can move away from burning fossil fuels is as important to our future welfare as the speed a pedestrian can muster in getting out of the way of an approaching truck. Until very recently, each year humanity burned more fossil fuel than the year before—the equivalent of walking towards the truck. But in 2014, the increase in our fossil fuel use stalled. We may no longer be walking towards danger, but when will we begin running towards safety?

Overall, I am optimistic that 2014 will be looked back on as the year the world turned its back on fossil fuels. One line of evidence that supports my optimism concerns the reduction of some very long-standing fossil-fuel subsidies. Historically low oil prices from the end of 2014 onwards allowed countries such as India, Indonesia and Peru to cut back their fossil-fuel subsidies without causing price rises. Without those subsidies, future rises in the oil price will surely impact on consumption by limiting demand. But even with oil prices low, the loss of subsidies leaves fossil fuels open to competition. For example, the use of kerosene for lighting is less attractive without subsidies, relative to the cost of a small solar lighting kit. In the wake of the post-Paris US–China Hangzhou Summit communiqué, announced in September 2016, the rate at which subsidies are scrapped is likely to increase sharply. Both the US and China are likely to include subsidy reduction in their lists of actions as pressure builds for the G20 to set a deadline for ending fossil fuel subsidies. Investment managers and insurers are adding pressure by calling for the deadline to be set soon. Mark Wilson, CEO of insurer Aviva, justifies the call by arguing that 'risk is magnified by the way in which fossil-fuel subsidies distort the energy market'.[1] Sadly, the issue did not make it onto the 2016 G20 Hangzhou communiqué, but despite the election of Donald Trump as the US president, the issue is unlikely to go away.

Another decisive shift that is likely to reduce fossil-fuel use has occurred in China, where the service sector is an increasingly important component of the economy. The service sector grew by 8.5 per cent in 2015, for the first time generating more than half of the nation's gross domestic product.[2] It is now clear that China has entered a far less energy intensive phase of its development than that of recent decades, and this should permit permanent reduction in the growth of demand for coal, and provide time for the economy to transition to clean energy generation.[3]

Things could have worked out very differently. There was a fear that low prices for coal and oil would stimulate a surge in investment in new polluting energy infrastructure, such as coal-fired power plants, as well as inhibiting the development of electric vehicles. But this did not happen. In fact, investments in clean energy technologies grew substantially during 2015—to a third of a trillion US dollars globally. Electric vehicles in particular are ramping up. China, for example, is on track to install more electric-vehicle charging points in the next five years than all of the rest of the world combined.[4] New markets for electric cars opened up in Mexico, Chile, South Africa and Morocco. Even in India government programs are helping create new markets for clean technology. The Indian coal tax and various incentives for solar PV meant that in 2016, for the first time, solar- and coal-based electricity were on a par in terms of cost. The economic advantage that wind and solar have in developed markets is nowhere more evident than in historically coal-dependent Australia, where 100 per cent of recent energy generation infrastructure has been renewable. Globally, 122 gigawatts of wind and solar were installed in 2015. Despite mooted developments like Adani's Carmichael coal mine in Australia, for the first time, clean technology accounted for around

50 per cent of all energy investm
2016 the International Energy Age
reported that electricity generated from renewa
sources (including hydroelectricity) exceeded that
from coal for the first time.[6]

With the costs of renewable energy continuing
to fall, and the 67 per cent decline in the cost of oil
failing to boost its use, along with prolonged low
prices and declining demand for coal, the future
seems clear. Though coal, oil and gas will doubtless
be burned for some decades to come, the fossil-fuel
era is gradually coming to a close. The only question
is whether the end will come quickly enough to save
the planet. Unfortunately, the outlook is not as good,
in part because formidable obstacles remain as we
push to ramp up the use of renewables.

The technologies that look set to replace, in the
near term, a significant proportion of fossil-fuel
generation are solar PV and wind. Both generate
electricity directly—solar PV by capturing and
moving electrons through a silica crystal lattice,
and wind by turning a turbine. Both have sustained

spectacular rates of growth over the past decade.

The number of solar PV panels installed globally has doubled every two years for last 14 years. By mid-2015, solar PV accounted for just 1 per cent of global electricity generation. But if it continued to double every two years for the next 12 years, enough solar panels would be installed globally to provide all the electricity humanity requires.[7] Such is the power of exponential growth. But of course this is unlikely to happen. In fact, problems are already emerging in areas where wind and solar PV provide a high proportion of electricity. That's because both wind and solar PV have an Achilles heel: the electricity they generate is only available intermittently—when the power sources of wind and/or sunlight are available. Until energy storage or other forms of clean energy generation become economically viable where wind and solar supply a large proportion of a region's electricity, they will require a commitment to backup power plants, which in most cases will be fuelled by gas, a fossil fuel. Gas plants last for 30 years, so increasing the uptake of wind and solar PV in regions where they already supply large proportions of the electricity is likely to lock us into gas-generated electricity for decades.

The dilemma posed by the rapid uptake of solar and wind was underlined recently in South Australia, where industries warned that the high price of electricity when it's not sunny and the wind isn't blowing may cause some major businesses to close.[8] In fact, high gas prices are as much to blame. Flaws in Australia's national electricity market, along with South Australia's poor grid connections with other states—and particularly the recent closure due to maintenance of a key interconnector—also fed into the problem. Despite these local factors, the issue does foreshadow a problem that's set to increase as wind and solar grow globally.

Indeed, concerns are already being voiced in California that a similar situation is developing there, and in the Hawaiian Islands regulators are limiting the licensing of new solar installations to avoid such a situation. Elon Musk, CEO of Tesla, proposed a novel solution to South Australia's electricity woes.

In 2017 he guaranteed to supply enough battery storage within 100 days to fix the problem, or he would supply the batteries for free.[9] Whether the offer is taken up, and what the price of the fix is, is yet to be revealed.

The problem of electricity intermittency from wind and solar is being used by proponents of nuclear power to argue that nuclear power has a role in future electricity generation. But for economic and safety reasons, the tide has now decisively turned against nuclear power, and its share of energy generation is declining globally. No doubt some established nuclear plants will continue to run for decades, and a few new plants will be built in countries such as China, where the government underwrites cost and assumes risk. But developments in renewable technology look set to make the need for nuclear power redundant.

There is a widespread assumption that energy storage technology in the form of batteries will arrive before the problem of intermittency of electricity supply from wind and solar grows too great.

This view is all too often based more on optimism than careful analysis. Furthermore, battery storage is not the only solution to the intermittency problem. We need to look at the development of other kinds of clean energy generation, in particular tidal, wave and geothermal power. By diversifying energy sources, it's theoretically possible to reduce or eliminate the intermittency of supply.

The power of tides can be used to generate electricity in places where tides are large and where the water can be dammed and diverted through turbines. South Korea has big plans for using tidal power, with proposed installations at Ganghwa Island, Incheon Bay and Garorim Bay, which together have the potential to generate more than 2000 megawatts of electricity. But the anticipated environmental costs are growing, and they look to be prohibitively high. The biggest problems concern the vast areas of highly productive tidal mud flats which will be degraded by impounding the water and the severe impacts that will have on fisheries and on endangered species, including migratory wading birds.[10]

The only other country contemplating tidal energy projects of more than 100 megawatts in scale is the UK, which in 2015 granted planning permission for a 320-megawatt facility near Swansea.

Wave power is far more widely available than tidal power, and significant technological advances have been made in harnessing it. One particularly promising technology is being trialled by Carnegie Wave Energy near Perth in Western Australia. It's of particular interest because most of the energy-generating infrastructure is on land, as well as in a buoy tethered to the sea floor, and is driven by fluid compressed by wave power, making maintenance easier and cheaper than traditional wave power. But for all its potential, wave power is at a far earlier stage of development than tidal power—all installations globally are either experimental or small scale, about a megawatt or less. The Carnegie Wave Energy array currently under development, however, is a 3-megawatt array (consisting of three 1-megawatt units), and because it is situated in an exceptionally favourable location it is projected to produce electricity continuously.[11] Recently, Carnegie Wave Energy committed to the construction of a two-stage, 15-megawatt wave energy facility at the Wave Hub in Cornwall, southwestern England. Carnegie hopes to have the first stage of the process finished by 2018.[12] When the entire project is complete this will be the world's largest wave energy facility.

Geothermal energy is a long-established and mainstream means of generating electricity, which works by using heat from inside the earth to create steam and drive turbines. Some countries, such as Iceland and the Philippines, which are rich in geothermal heat, derive more than 15 per cent of their current electricity generation from it. Yet by 2015, geothermal energy was generating only about 12.5 gigawatts of electricity globally, though it was growing at around 5 per cent per year.[13] Compared with solar PV's doubling of capacity every two years, this growth rate looks feeble. One limitation faced by wave, tidal and geothermal energy is that all are available only where especially favourable conditions prevail. It's possible that technological breakthroughs might allow any of these renewable technologies to grow substantially, but their geographic limitations make it seem highly unlikely that the scale of their deployment will ever match wind or solar PV.

The relentless decrease in the cost of electricity generated by solar PV and wind has spawned optimism that storage technologies, in particular batteries, will follow the same cost-reduction pathway, and within a decade or so will become cheap enough to combine with wind and solar PV to provide continuously available electricity, which will provide not only for stationary energy needs, but for transport as well. The confidence in this outcome has seen vast sums of money invested in battery technology. But battery technology is not the only way to store electricity.

There are three forms of bulk energy storage:

1. Mechanical, such as pumped storage (where water pumped uphill can then flow back down to turn a turbine), compressed air or a flywheel.

2. Heat or cold, such as hot-water systems or liquid salt.
3. Electrochemical, such as batteries.

Currently, large volumes of energy are stored mechanically worldwide, principally through pumping water up into dams using sources such as wind power when it is in excess supply. But storing energy as heat, as well as in batteries, is becoming a very big business. One of the key questions for our future concerns how these storage methods stack up against each other, and against other options. There are many factors determining which option prevails in any given locality, but among the most important are availability, reliability and cost. Pumping water into dams when excess generation capacity is available from either wind or solar is very cheap. Indeed, not doing it can mean wasting clean energy. But dams are not available everywhere, and where they are, the capacity for hydroelectric generation can be limited. And, of course, there are as yet few parts of the world where wind and solar capacity result in a significant energy oversupply that can be stored.

Batteries have been in use for 200 years, and a considerable diversity of types exists. In recent years there has been huge investment in battery technology, and lithium-ion batteries (which are energy dense and can be recharged many times) lead the field by a substantial margin. This has led to significant increases in efficiency (40 per cent in the five years to 2014), mostly from small adjustments in the production process. By 2014, approximately 200 megawatts of storage capacity in lithium-ion batteries existed worldwide. This will doubtless grow swiftly, in part because battery costs have fallen by an average of 14 per cent every year between 2007 and 2014. Indeed there are hopes that Tesla's 'gigafactory' in Nevada will be producing half a million lithium-ion batteries per year for electric vehicles by 2020, which would drive further decreases in cost.[14] But even if mass storage of energy in electric vehicle batteries that can return energy to the electricity network when required does eventuate, there is still likely to be insufficient storage in the energy sector for at least a decade. And with 90 million fossil-fuel-burning cars manufactured annually, massive growth in electric vehicles must occur before they begin to displace internal combustion engines. Based on current cost analyses, I think that batteries will remain an expensive option for energy storage, relative to many mechanical and heat-storage options, for at least another decade and perhaps longer.

Fundamental breakthroughs that could change this scenario seem far into the future, if indeed they will emerge at all. But because breakthroughs are always possible, it's worth looking at a couple of possibilities that have recently come to prominence. Lithium-air batteries, which use atmospheric oxygen rather than a solid material to run, offer a much lighter storage solution than conventional lithium-ion storage. Theoretically, they can provide the highest efficiency possible from a battery. But from a technical point of view they are extremely challenging, and a recent decline in patenting of lithium-air batteries suggests that research interest is waning, so it's likely to be many years, if ever, before they are produced commercially at scale.[15] The development of magnesium batteries is also being pursued. They are smaller and denser in terms of stored energy per gram than current lithium-ion batteries but, like lithium air, they are still in the early developmental stage.

One often-overlooked means of chemical storage involves the production of hydrogen. Hydrogen is not a primary source of energy, but rather a way to store energy. The production method using clean energy involves decomposing molecules of water to create hydrogen and oxygen. Around 40 per cent of the energy put into the process can be recovered from the hydrogen. The hydrogen business is already very large, with some 57 million tonnes of hydrogen produced annually, around half of which goes into the production of agricultural fertilisers, and most of the rest to treating heavy oils to make them more useable.[16] Unfortunately, 96 per cent of all hydrogen is currently derived from fossil fuels, mostly gas. But, as mentioned above, hydrogen can also be produced from clean sources, and the large-scale deployment of wind and solar

PV technologies is opening new opportunities for a so-called 'hydrogen economy'.[17] In some regions, wind and solar PV are producing more electricity at certain times than can be used or stored. And it is this excess electricity, which is essentially free, that is being stored as hydrogen derived from the decomposition of water. This involves a process called electrolysis, in which an electric current is passed through water, breaking the bonds linking the hydrogen and oxygen in the H_2O. While hydrogen production using hydrolysis remains more expensive than generating hydrogen from fossil fuels, costs are declining as methods improve.

The process of electrolysis was discovered by the pioneering chemist and physicist Michael Faraday more than 150 years ago, and with the recent development of cheap, clean energy, it's becoming an important process in our transition away from fossil fuels. That's because the hydrogen it generates can be used as a substitute for fossil fuel in many uses. For example, it can be used in household-based fuel cells instead of electricity from coal-fired power plants.

It can also be used in transport, or can be converted into hythane gas to augment (and compete with) the natural gas supply.[18] It can even be used to make agricultural fertilisers.

The use of hydrogen in transport is progressing rapidly. Until a decade ago, it was thought that hydrogen would have to be transported from a central processing facility, using tankers or pipelines, to provide fuel for hydrogen-powered vehicles. But, more recently, it's been realised that the hydrogen can be produced locally through small electrolysis plants at refuelling points, using grid-based electricity. The current global leaders in hydrogen-vehicle technology are the Japanese and Korean manufacturers Toyota, Honda and Hyundai, and the German company Mercedes-Benz, all of whom have vehicles on the market powered by fuel cells. The German government is also manufacturing a fuel-cell-powered submarine. As mentioned, an alternative use for the hydrogen is the manufacture of ammonia for use in agricultural fertilisers. Currently, fertilisers are made from natural gas, and around 180 million tonnes are produced from fossil fuels per annum, so the use of hydrogen derived from wind or solar PV would create a much greener solution by avoiding the use of fossil fuels.

With so many potential uses for hydrogen, and with a growing excess of electricity from wind and solar PV, there is a lot of interest in hydrogen technologies. I am certain that hydrogen will hasten the end of fossil fuels, especially gas. But the extent to which hydrogen storage will be able to act as a 'battery' for our energy needs is yet to be determined. The fossil fuel that is often claimed to be a bridge to a clean-energy future is gas. To what extent can it be used as a battery-like buffer (albeit a dirty one) as we transition to renewables? Gas can be burned to generate electricity at times when wind and solar aren't meeting demand. So, from a market perspective, gas and renewables must be compared with renewables with storage. In fact, one option being investigated to solve South Australia's intermittency woes is for the government to build a gas-fired power plant that will remain on standby and be called upon when clean-energy provision falters.

The use of gas for electricity generation in the US has been spectacular because very cheap gas derived from fracking shales has been available. One consequence is that it has outcompeted coal in the electricity sector. Indeed, in the 12 months to January 2016, the amount of electricity in the US supplied by gas was larger than that supplied by coal.[19] Recently, gas prices in the US have risen, to around US $3 per 1000 cubic feet. And production growth is slowing, to only 1 per cent in 2015. Globally, demand for gas is also slowing, despite low prices.[20]

In Europe, gas prices have been relatively high and so gas is rarely burned at any scale to generate electricity. Moreover, a major source is gas piped in from Russia, which presents its own political difficulties. This situation has opened the door to the possibility of gasifying or burning biomass at scale, to be used at times of high energy demand. Germany is a leader in this form of electricity supply, with 5000 megawatts of installed capacity at the end of 2013 (though growth in installed capacity has slowed greatly in the past two years).[21] Despite such innovations, it is possible that the rapid growth of intermittent sources of electricity from wind and solar will, unless storage catches up quickly, lock us into the construction of many gas-fired power plants that will pollute for decades to come, in order to supply electricity when renewables are not generating.

Storing energy as heat is yet another option, and recent developments mean that it offers what I think is our best hope of changing direction and so avoiding the gas trap. But we will need a very different kind of storage from that used most commonly up to now. Heat storage has a long history, particularly in the storage of low-quality heat for the purpose of heating houses. Heat energy can even be stored in the ground in summer to be used in winter, such as is done at Drake Landing in Alberta, Canada.[22] There are, however, more recent energy technologies—Concentrated Solar Thermal (CST)—which allow for the storage of high-quality heat (at temperatures greater than 500°C), and it is these that offer our best hope of a near-term 100 per cent clean-energy future.

CHAPTER 4

The Unique Power of Concentrated Sunlight

One of the most recent clean energy technologies to come to commercial scale is Concentrated Solar Thermal (CST), which involves concentrating the energy of sunlight to create high-quality heat. Millions of people the world over use solar thermal hot water systems (a technology pioneered in Australia). But the new CST technologies are very different. They are industrial-scale power plants that can generate and store very high-temperature (in excess of 550°C) heat, and therefore run after the sun goes down.

In the great portfolio of renewable energy technologies currently available to us, CST stands out as being uniquely useful in addressing the multiple challenges humanity faces in providing for its needs in coming decades. Because the industry is at an early stage of technological development, it provides a useful example of the many problems any new technology faces as its backers strive to grow it to economic scale in a cleaner global economy.

There are many, many ways of concentrating sunlight to create high-quality heat, and a great diversity of CST power plant types have been built and are operating. This diversity is characteristic of an immature industry. In mature industries, one or a few types of technology have over time proven superior and so have come to dominate. CST is immature and is having lots of teething problems. For example, some plants have cost far more to build than planned, and others are operating far less efficiently than envisaged, while yet others are accident-prone or are having unexpected environmental impacts. These various obstacles, along with the increasing competitiveness of wind and solar, are causing some investors to abandon CST. That is very unfortunate, for the technology desperately needs immediate investment if it is to mature quickly. Indeed, in light of the intermittency problem, a case can be made that investment in CST should be increased relative to PV and wind. But, in fact, the opposite is happening.

Despite its teething problems, CST has two attributes that make it indispensable in our struggle for a better future. First, most kinds of CST can store energy and so can generate electricity and heat, and even produce freshwater, in the absence of direct sunlight. Second, they offer the simplest and most efficient means we currently have of doing this. These characteristics are just what we need if we are to feed, power and clean up a world in which 9 billion people can sustainably live in coming decades.

The heat generated by CST can be used for many things. Through flash distillation, it can desalinate seawater to provide freshwater or clean up polluted water to provide pure freshwater for human consumption or crops. The steam it generates can be used to clean polluted soils, and, in some technology types, the heat it can generate is sufficiently high-grade to break up the CO_2 molecule itself, leading to new possibilities in manufacturing. Despite these possibilities, CST is still widely thought of principally in terms of electricity generation.

All of the larger CST plants are of two fundamental types, known as trough or tower. In trough CST, sunlight is focussed onto a tube which runs through parabolic troughs. The tube, which runs for many kilometres, contains a salt fluid that is capable of absorbing the heat of the collected sunlight. The superhot liquid salt is then stored in insulated tanks for later use in heating water to provide steam to generate electricity. At a distance, these 'solar fields' don't look too different from fields filled with solar panels, but they operate very differently: they concentrate and collect heat rather than directly generating electricity. The tower CST plants can look almost space-age, with elevated, glowing heat absorbers that are visible for kilometres around. They work by focussing the sunlight reflected in thousands of mirrors onto a heat absorber mounted on a tower, through which flows the heat-absorbing fluid.

Both trough- and tower-type CST plants use their hot fluid to create steam to turn a turbine, and so generate electricity.

Because we need electricity to be available on demand, energy storage is central to a decarbonised future. But how much storage is needed? It turns out that the human electricity demand has a remarkable similarity across the world. Whether it's a large city, or a small African village, demand is highest in the morning and evening. In the small hours, demand drops to a minimum. This drop means that CST systems don't need to store 12 hours of daytime-level supply—and many CST plants aren't designed to provide 12 hours of storage. The Magaldi STEM, for example, can provides for just six hours of maximum demand after sunset. In the real world, where people sleep instead of work or play for at least part of the night, this is usually sufficient to last for 12 hours.

CST plants require a lot of direct, strong sunlight, so they cannot be built everywhere. But huge expanses of the planet—extending from the southern fringes of western Canada in the north, through to most of the lower 48 states of the USA, central and South America, and most of Africa, Asia and Australia—offer sufficient sunlight for CST. The best areas, however, are often in deserts or at high elevation, with the western US, north-western Argentina, the Sahara, the Middle East and Western Australia offering ideal conditions.

Despite the wide geographic area suitable for CST plants, most existing plants are located in just two countries: Spain and the USA. All five of the world's larger CST plants (with 250 megawatts or more of capacity) are located in the US, while 13 of the world's 16 plants of between 100 and 200 mega-watts of capacity are located in Spain (the remaining four are in the United Arab Emirates, Morocco, South Africa and the USA). It is important to understand that when we talk of a plant rated at 250 megawatts, for example, it means that the plant is capable, under ideal conditions, of producing 250 megawatts of electricity (a watt being a unit of power—1 joule per second). There are also many smaller CST plants scattered across a large number of countries, some of which offer interesting innovations over the standard technologies used in the larger plants.[1]

Because one of the primary objectives of almost all CST technology is to store energy so that it is available after dark, they need to be able to generate steam after the sun goes down. So during the day they collect far more sunlight (and thus have a larger number of solar collectors) than a system designed only to run during the day. For example, if a CST plant needs to generate energy at full capacity for eight hours after sunset, it would need to have twice as many solar collectors as one that runs only while the sun shines. And this, of course involves an extra cost.[2]

Another cost involves the fluid that carries the heat and the tanks necessary to store the heated fluid. None of this is required in solar PV, and it understandably makes CST more expensive, in terms of electricity generated, than solar PV. But then, without expensive batteries, solar PV cannot store energy. Batteries are improving and the cost is coming down, but it will be many years, if ever, before PV with batteries can produce cheaper electricity than CST.

Different heat-conveying fluids are used in the various plants. On the surface, the choice of fluid might seem to be a simple matter: why not use water? Some CST plants, including the very largest ever built, do use water to convey heat. But at the atmospheric pressure at sea-level, water boils at 100°C and the steam it then turns into can build up great pressure, making it difficult to contain over tens of kilometres of piping. One innovative type of CST plant even uses compressed air, but that also can be difficult to contain, especially when heated to 1000°C.

A more common solution is to use a mixture of salts as the heat-conducting fluid. A mixture of sodium nitrate, potassium nitrate and calcium nitrate melts, and so becomes liquid, at about 131°C.

Lithium salts, which have an even lower melting point of 116°C, have also been used experimentally. Another alternative is the use of diathermic (heat absorbing) oil. But each of these fluids has its own limitations, drawbacks and costs. Molten salts are expensive, costing around US $1000 per tonne. And an average power plant requires 30,000 tonnes of salt. That's a $30 million investment for each power plant—which can exceed 10 per cent of the cost of the plant as a whole.[3]

In plants such as Archimede in Sicily (one of the first large-scale CST plants to be built), the use of diathermic oil proved to be less efficient for conveying heat than liquid salts.[4] And at US$2–3 per litre in parts of Europe, diathermic oil is even more expensive than molten salts.

The very first commercial-scale power plant to use liquid salt was the parabolic trough-type Archimede facility at Prio Gargallo, near Syracuse in Sicily. Syracuse is the birthplace of Archimedes, who famously used mirrors to focus the heat of the sun on the ships of invading Romans, setting them alight while at sea. The Archimede CST plant was one of the first modern CST plants to be completed. It began commercial operations in 2010 and consists of nearly five and a half kilometres of parabolic troughs and tubing. At Archimede, the salt is heated to 550°C, a temperature that allows for the creation of very high-quality steam to drive a turbine.[5] Archimede generates approximately 5 megawatts of electricity (enough to power about 1000 houses), and can store sufficient heat to run at full capacity for eight hours after the sun goes down.[6] But Archimede is not entirely renewable. It is coupled with a gas-fired power plant, and there are very good reasons for this. The first concerns one of the biggest drawbacks of using the otherwise highly efficient molten salt to convey the heat. If the temperature of the salt ever drops below its melting point it solidifies and the entire system of tubing needs to be replaced, at enormous cost. One expert has identified this as one of the greatest drawbacks of the parabolic trough type of plant:

> Detractors of molten salt parabolic trough systems will point to two drawbacks…The primary concern is the chance of a molten salt freeze-out in the 50–150 kilometres of receiver lines and header pipes that a large solar field has. The second argument is that it is much harder to get to these high temperatures…especially in not so perfect solar resource areas…Another way of phrasing this is that high temperature results in lower efficiency of the parabolic trough collector due to the higher heat losses.[7]

A run of cloudy days can easily see the salts cool to their freezing point, so gas (or some other form of energy, such as biomass) is essential to boost the temperature of the molten salt if it looks like the salts are approaching their freezing point. In some power plants, gas is also used to heat the system in the morning to allow efficient function at dawn.

The other CST design-type currently in use in large-scale CST plants is the tower type. These plants use mirrors to focus the rays of the sun onto a heat-absorbing receiver, which sits atop the tower. A fluid is circulated and heated within the receiver, and is then used to transfer the heat to a steam-driven turbine, where electricity is created. Some of the mirrors are located at a considerable distance from the tower, so highly sophisticated technology is required to keep the mirrors precisely focussed on the receivers. The Ivanpah CST plant is a tower type and is located in the Mojave Desert about 60 kilometres southwest of Las Vegas. Commissioned in 2014, it consists of three towers, each 145 metres tall, surrounded by 173,500 solar reflectors that collectively cover an area of 1600 hectares. It is currently the largest CST plant in the world and is theoretically capable of generating 392 megawatts of power. It is unusual in that it uses water (as steam) rather than molten salt to convey the heat away from the tower's collector.

This highly innovative power-plant design has suffered a number of problems, among which, rather surprisingly, is a strong dependence on fossil fuels. The plant is designed to commence its daily activities by burning natural gas for an hour before dawn, so that it will operate effectively come sunrise. But instead of requiring an hour of gas consumption, it needs four to reach the required heat. As a result, in 2014 it emitted 46,084 tonnes of CO_2. It also generated a total of 524,000 megawatt hours of electricity. If the gas had been burned to generate electricity directly, it would have generated about a quarter as much (124,000 megawatt hours). Things improved in 2015, in that substantially less gas was burned per unit of electricity. But the fundamental problems remain: the plant requires a lot more steam to run smoothly than originally planned for, and it turns out that, as a result of the contrails from jet aircraft and clouds, there's less sunlight than anticipated.[8]

One final and rather appalling problem has emerged at Ivanpah. Large numbers of dead birds with charred feathers have been discovered in the vicinity of the plant. Researchers believe that they were burned alive while flying through the intense heat of the reflected sunlight. In April 2015, biologists working for the State of California estimated that in the previous 12 months 3500 birds had died this way. The smoking bird carcases workers see shooting from the vicinity of the tower are so frequent they're referred to as 'streamers'.

In early 2016 a similar problem emerged at the Crescent Dunes CST plant in Nevada. The tower-type plant can generate up to 110 megawatts of electricity, and had been operating commercially since September 2015. Until 14 January that year, as the plant prepared for power generation each day, the 3000 reflectors had been maintained in a 'standby' position in which the reflectors focussed on a point above the heat absorber, creating an intense zone of heat in the air that was visible in the form of a halo. But on 14 January 2015, 115 birds were seen to fly into the halo and burst into flames.

Engineers discovered that the problem could be easily rectified by altering the 'standby' position of the reflectors so that no hot spot is created.[9] This, however, may prove to be simply one dimension of a larger problem involving birds and tower-type CST plants. It appears likely that birds are attracted to insects drawn to the glowing light of the towers. When in the vicinity of the plant, they are at risk of being burned or colliding with reflectors. At Ivanpah, a variety of birds, including peregrine falcons, barn owls and yellow-rumped warblers, have perished. As a result, the operators have undertaken or planned a variety of measures to discourage birds from the area, including avian radars (which are used at airports), the covering of ponds to make them inaccessible to birds, and the clearing of natural vegetation in the vicinity of the site.[10]

It remains to be seen how effective these measures will be. In the meantime other problems have emerged. On 19 May 2016, for example, the Ivanpah plant set itself alight when its reflectors became misaligned (an accident that emphasises the extreme precision required to focus the mirrors over great distances), forcing one of the three towers to shut down. Almost all new technologies have teething problems, and Ivanpah is clearly no exception. But despite these, it must be said that great strides forward have been made. For example, water use at Ivanpah has been reduced by 90 per cent and operational efficiency has increased. But this has not been enough to avoid a flight of investors from Ivanpah and similar CST projects. Overcoming problems is expensive. Professor Lucas Davis from the University of California, Berkeley, sees this as a major factor, along with the competitiveness of solar PV, inhibiting future investment in the US at least: 'I don't expect a lot of solar thermal to get built. It's just too expensive.'[11]

Recent incidents at tower plants elsewhere in the world have added to the concern. On 15 June 2016 a leak of molten sodium salts (which combust on contact with the air) caused a fire at a pilot plant at Jemalong near the town of Forbes in New South Wales, causing the evacuation of some nearby houses. The opening of the one-megawatt tower-type pilot plant (a precursor to a planned 30-megawatt facility), built by Veste Power, was delayed by some months as a result.[12]

Two newer approaches to CST, both currently operating only at small scale, may offer significant advantages over existing systems. One of the advantages offered by both systems is their modular construction. So, instead of having to commit to building a single massive CST plant, companies can build as few or as many smaller modules as can be afforded or are required. The technologies discussed below are at an extremely immature stage, and many technical difficulties will doubtless arise and need to be resolved. Both, however, in my view hold considerable promise.

The first of these technologies, Heliofocus, was developed in Israel. It operates by facing a parabolic dish (like a radio-telescope dish), itself consisting of 500 square metres of curved mirrors, to the sun, and concentrating its rays onto a collector. Pressurised air, which can be heated as high as 1000°C by the concentrated rays, is then used to create steam and generate electricity. The Heliofocus system is highly efficient, requires only a small land area, and is said to generate electricity cheaply.[13] The system, however, does not appear to have the capacity to store energy. At the time of writing, no commercial Heliofocus plant was operational, but a 0.5-megawatt plant was under construction in Israel, and a 1-megawatt plant was being commissioned in Inner Mongolia. Clearly this technology is at a very early stage. Only time will tell whether the difficulties of managing superheated, pressurised air and the current lack of storage capability will stymie this otherwise promising approach.

The second of these very new systems is known as STEM (Solar Thermo-Electric Magaldi). It was developed by Magaldi Industries near Salerno, Italy. STEM uses a field of parabolic mirrors to reflect sunlight onto a mirror mounted above a receiver. This double reflection system avoids the need for a tall tower and its associated problems, but does slightly decrease efficiency. However, STEM requires no fluid or associated piping for storing the heat, which represents a fundamental breakthrough. Instead, the concentrated sunlight is used to heat sand—to 600°C. Since October 2015 I have been chief scientific advisor to Magaldi Solar. This means that I know the technology well, but because it is difficult to objectively evaluate a technology I'm so intimately familiar with, I want to declare this up front so that readers can factor it in as they read about STEM.

Currently, there is only one commercial-scale STEM unit in operation, located at San Filippo del Melo, in Sicily. The entire plant covers an area of 2.5 hectares, most of which is the reflector field. In terms of area, this is much the same, per megawatt of energy produced, as that of trough and tower technologies. The plant at San Filippo can generate two megawatts of heat, another 0.5 megawatt of electricity, and can provide electricity at full capacity for six hours after the sun goes down.

STEM is fundamentally different from other CST technologies. The sunlight does not have to be as precisely focussed nor be as concentrated as it passes from the solar field to the secondary mirror. The most distant reflector is only 90 metres from the secondary mirror, and the maximum air temperature reached is 80°C, meaning that birds should be safer. During the construction of the STEM plant, a discovery was made that could have set the project back for year, but was turned to advantage. The remains of the oldest port city in Sicily were discovered on the construction site. This meant that no digging could occur without vast expense and time in order to care for the excavated remains. So the engineers decided not to excavate at all. Instead they used concrete blocks to anchor the mirrors, and developed extremely smart technology to permit their alignment, even as the blocks settled on the land surface.

But, arguably, the most innovative part of the STEM system is the use of sand to absorb and store heat. Sand has excellent insulating properties, meaning that it normally loses heat slowly. But if you 'fluidise' it by blowing air through the grains so that the sand acts like a liquid, it becomes highly conductive. Fluidising the sand during the sunlight hours of the day allows the heat to be captured, and when the air jets are turned off the heat will stay in the sand for days without significant loss. In order to get the heat out, part of the sand-bed is fluidised, thereby releasing the heat, which can be used to create steam. A key aspect of the STEM system is its simplicity. It consists of nothing but steel, glass and sand, and being modular it can be built at any scale. Full figures will not be available for a couple of years, but preliminary data suggest that STEM performs financially at least as well as the large trough and tower systems. Moreover the basic unit has the potential to be modified to suit different purposes, depending on whether more heat or electricity is required and how much storage is needed.

In late 2016 the sole operating STEM plant was closed to allow it to be reconfigured to optimise efficiency. The reconfigured plant is expected to resume operations in 2017. Mario Magaldi, the inventor of the system, makes a poetic observation on STEM, saying, 'the alchemists of old wanted to turn lead into gold. When sand is heated to 600°C, it glows a beautiful golden colour. Perhaps it is the elusive transformation humanity has so long searched for.'

Magaldi's observation appears prescient in light of the astonishing diversity of problems and opportunities that CST technologies may well go on to address. From food production to cleaning

up soil and water pollution, and on to the manufacture of carbon fibre, CST has the potential to
play an important role. The unique capacities that
heat, electricity and large-scale storage capacity can
deliver are impressive. But CST is an immature
technology. With more STEM system units being
commissioned, within a few years we should know
whether or not STEM really is the breakthrough
that will drive CST to maturity.

CHAPTER 5
Sullied Soils and Waters

In the early phases of the industrial revolution, pollution was a severe problem in parts of Europe and the USA, with the Thames being perhaps the most polluted of all rivers. In 1855, Michael Faraday described it as 'an opaque pale brown fluid... surely the river ought not to be allowed to become a fermenting sewer.'[1]

Sadly, Faraday's call went unheeded and by 1950, after a century and a half of industrialisation, scientists from London's Natural History Museum declared the Thames at London to be biologically dead. There were no fish, and there was no oxygen.

Beginning in the 1960s, better regulation and investments in infrastructure such as sewers have seen the concentration of raw sewage, heavy metals and other pollutants drop to the point that today the Thames is the cleanest river to run through any major European city. Seals now cavort around Canary Wharf, while dolphins, porpoises and even whales are occasionally sighted at Westminster.[2] Despite the cleaning up of the Thames and many other highly polluted rivers in Europe and North America, the problems of soil, air and water pollution continue to grow globally at a rapid rate. The brief review of the nature and severity of the pollution problem presented in this chapter is framed with an eye to answering the question of what is required to restore the most polluted regions of Earth to health. For unless we achieve that, our prospects of feeding a world with a population of 9 billion are remote indeed.

In 2012, I spent two months in China, making a documentary. The work took me far and wide, but while the country and its people varied greatly from place to place, a few things remained constant.

From the Great Wall in the north to Shanghai in the south, and westwards to Chengdu, a brown fug hung in the atmosphere. In some places the air had a sharp metallic tang, in others a foetid faecal odour, depending on the prevailing local pollution. Often the precise stench altered with the wind. Just occasionally, the air was clear, such as in Hong Kong after a typhoon. I particularly remember one crystal-clear morning in Beijing. It had snowed overnight, and for a few hours the atmosphere was glorious. But you only had to look down at the footpath, or at the passing cars, to see where the pollution had gone. Everything was covered in the grime that was being released by the melting snow. Having breathed the foul atmosphere for days, my lungs, I realised, must be the same black colour as the pavement.

Shortly afterwards I visited the section of the environment department charged with measuring the pollution and cleaning up Beijing's air. They said that they were optimistic, given time, that the mess could be cleaned up. But they had no illusions about the immensity of the task. The pollution sources were many and varied, from the city's ever-growing vehicle fleet to a vast variety of factories, and on to construction sites and dust from overexploited and desertified lands. Come back in 10 years, one researcher said, and you might see a difference.

According to the UN, 'declining water quality has become a global issue of concern...Every day, two million tons of sewage and other effluents drain into the world's waters'. As a result, 'every year, more people die from unsafe water than from all forms of violence, including war'.[3] Sadly, the truth of this statement was abundantly clear during my visit to China. On the Huangpu River (a distributary of the Yangtze that passes Shanghai at its famed Bund) it was painful to see the thousands of dead fish floating in the stream. Weeks before our visit, the river had carried the bodies of 10,000 dead pigs that had been dumped into the water. The Huang Po is Shanghai's water supply.

The Yellow River, which is the third-longest river in Asia, is in even worse shape than the Huang Po. Its flow is so severely depleted by human exploitation that it frequently fails to reach the sea. And 10 per cent of its remaining volume is raw effluent. For about a third of its length, industrial and other pollutants have made the river unfit for any human use whatsoever.[4] Until we ascended the foothills of the Himalaya at Jo Zai Go, I don't recall seeing a body of freshwater, whether it was a pond, lake or river, that was not severely polluted.

As appalling as its air and water pollution problems are, there is a third pollution problem in China that is possibly even more ominous. Often referred to as China's hidden pollution crisis, it concerns the state of the nation's soils. Due to China's appallingly unchecked and unmanaged industrialisation, many different types of pollutants have found their way into the nation's soils, particularly its agricultural soils, and so much secrecy exists around the issue that it's difficult to grasp the true extent of the problem. One of the most widespread and dangerous kinds of soil pollution for which at least some documentation exists, however, is cadmium. This element illustrates how industrial pollution finds its way from factory to soil and into food—it is emblematic of the problems facing the nation's soils as a whole.

A heavy metal, cadmium is extremely toxic to humans and other animal life. Even in small amounts it can result in severe health problems, including damage to lungs, kidneys, bones and liver. It is also a known carcinogen. Globally, about half a million people are thought to suffer from cadmium poisoning.[5]

Cadmium moves readily from the soil into food crops. It is appalling to learn, therefore, that 19.4 per cent of China's agricultural soils are heavily contaminated with various pollutants, of which cadmium, nickel and arsenic are the most prevalent.[6] The situation around Tai Lake near Suzhou in central China illustrates how the problem manifests. Lake Tai, at 1300 square kilometres, is China's third-largest lake and was long celebrated for its abundant aquatic resources, including the hairy mitten crab, a Chinese delicacy. The region around the lake was also long known for its pottery, particularly a heavy brown-glazed type prized for teapots. In the last few decades the industry has grown enormously, with over 3000 factories (a large number of which manufacture ceramics) having been established around the lake. Tragically, heavy metals, including cadmium, are used in various production processes, with pottery production being a particularly large user. The pollution is initially emitted in the form of gas or as contaminated water and sludge, which readily enters the lake. As a result, today the once clear waters of Lake Tai look like soy sauce, and the lake has become more famous for its foul-smelling, toxic algal blooms than its seafood.

Analysis by China's environment protection agency has revealed that the most severe pollutants in Lake Tai are cadmium, lead and mercury. All are bio-accumulating—living things avidly absorb and retain them, and then concentrate them up the food chain. But so concentrated is the pollution that even the levels of toxins low down the food chain—in plants—can be appallingly high. Cadmium levels of 0.5 milligrams per kilogram—almost three times the legal limit—have been recorded in rice grown around Lake Tai. Similar problems have emerged in other regions, including Hunan, famous for its rice production. Official figures (which may be an underestimate) indicate that nationwide China produces 12 million tonnes of heavy-metal-contaminated grain per year, out of an annual crop of about 600 million tonnes.

The problem around Lake Tai was long known to the local people. Wu Lihong, a former factory salesman, had been fighting for a clean-up of the pollution for nearly a decade when, in 2005, he was hailed as an 'environmental warrior' at China's National People's Congress. Just two years later, in 2007, he was arrested and jailed for three years for his activities, during which time he received brutal treatment—presumably at the behest of industrialists running polluting enterprises and their allies in the provincial government. With increasing levels of pollution, however, the Chinese government committed to action. They forced the closure, relocation or re-tooling of over 500 factories around Lake Tai. But the pollution legacy is vast and, sadly, the contamination problem continues to worsen. Think of soils as blotting paper and a polluting factory as a dropper filled with ink suspended above it. Many factories may have stopped adding pollution, but enormous concentrations of cadmium have accumulated in soils around the polluting factories, and water and living organisms continue to spread the toxins, at extremely dangerous concentrations, through the landscape long after the closures—just as the ink continues to spread through the blotting paper long after the dropper is removed.

Soil pollution is perhaps the most poorly understood and hidden of all of Earth's pollution problems. Globally, the quality of data on polluted soils is poor, so the full extent of the problem is not apparent. But the situation in Europe, where reporting is better than it is in China—and indeed most places—gives some indication of how large the problem is. The Global Soil Forum (GSF), which is part of the Institute for Advanced Sustainability Studies in Potsdam, says that 342,000 contaminated sites have been identified within Europe, and that so far only

80,000 of them have been cleaned up. The institute admits that much data is lacking, with the precise extent and severity of salt and acid contamination in particular yet to be fully assessed. The forum contends that the most important contaminants in recorded sites are mineral oils and heavy metals, including lead, arsenic, cadmium and mercury, which together account for 60 per cent of all soil contamination identified in Europe.[7]

How severe are the health effects of soil pollution? Coming into contact with polluted soils—either through touching it, breathing in dust blown from it or eating food grown in it—can cause kidney and skeletal disease, brain damage and cancer. More than a billion people worldwide—one-seventh of the world's population—are thought to suffer from lead poisoning, much of it coming from soils. Lead poisoning can be passed from mother to child in breast milk and is particularly damaging to growing brains. It can exacerbate schizophrenia and violent behaviour. Add that to the millions more who suffer from poisoning by arsenic, cadmium, mercury and other heavy metals, and some idea of the human cost of the soil-pollution problem becomes clear.

Cleaning soils is a formidable task. Even where clean-ups are underway, the problem grows. The cost of managing Europe's contaminated soils is around 6 billion Euros annually. And, sadly, despite the expenditure, the Global Soil Forum claims that the danger is increasing, with the number of recorded polluted sites across Europe expected to increase by 50 per cent by 2025.

Air, water and soil pollution are interrelated and cannot be addressed in isolation. I have no doubt that China will tackle its myriad pollution problems with vigour. For instance, China's dramatic shift away from coal as an energy source marks an impressive start. Coal burning is the source of about half the world's mercury pollution. But the shift must be accompanied by far more vigorous and determined action. Increasingly, the Chinese people are becoming aware of the dangers pollution poses, as evidenced by their preference for imported foodstuffs. Even the people living around Lake Tai are reluctant to eat the food grown there. I have the distinct feeling that the Chinese see their country as a land of undrinkable water, inedible food, unbreathable air, and that this threatens the government's 'mandate of heaven'—its right to rule. Since 2014, there has been increased transparency about the scale and nature of various kinds of pollution, from the Chinese government. If the Communist Party of China wishes to survive, it will need to act fast in dealing with the nation's appalling environmental pollution.

China is home to one-fifth of humanity, but it is not alone in facing an almost intolerable burden of pollution. India, the second most-populous nation, after China, is also severely polluted. A 2016 World Health Organization survey of air quality listed four Indian cities (Gwalior, Allahabad, Patna and Raipur) as among the seven most polluted urban areas on Earth. The capital, Delhi, ranked 11th and the list was topped by Zabol, in Iran.[8] The sources of India's pollution differ from those in China and so the challenges presented differ too. On the subcontinent, industrial pollutants are a relatively minor contributor to air pollution, while motorised vehicles and the burning of biomass emit the lion's share. Much of the pollution-generating biomass is burned in cook stoves in the 100-million Indian households that are totally dependent on them. As far as fossil fuels go, by far the worst offenders are the innumerable vehicles powered by 2-stroke motors that often use highly polluting adulterated fuels, and perpetual traffic jams considerably exacerbate the problem.

India's water-pollution problems also differ from those in China. India's mother river, the Ganges, is as renowned for the filth it carries as its holiness. Five hundred million people live on its banks, 114 cities discharge raw sewage and partially cremated bodies into it, and around 2 million bathe in its waters daily. As you might suspect, India's single largest water pollution problem is not industrial but human waste. Although a huge problem, the Indian government is serious about cleaning up these sources of pollution, and an ongoing program of providing treatment plants and diverting the waste is underway.

Regionally, however, industrial toxins do add to water pollution in India. An investigation by the Postgraduate Institute of Medical and Education Research (PGIMER) in Chandigarh, Punjab, revealed high levels of lead and cadmium, among other heavy metals, in water around the burgeoning industrial city of Ludhiana. As India industrialises this problem is bound to grow.[9]

Even in developed countries severe pollution can exist, such as that within the so called 'triangle of death' between Nola, Acerra and Marigliano in the Campania region near Naples, Italy, with a population of around 1.5 million. Beginning in the 1980s, the Mafia, having secured lucrative garbage disposal contracts, began dumping industrial wastes, mostly at night, right across the region. By 2013, 10 million tonnes—much of it highly toxic— had been dumped.[10] The result is an epidemic of birth defects, elevated rates of some cancers, and possibly premature ageing, throughout the region.[11]

The problem has become so severe that the Italian army has been sent in to prevent further dumping of toxic waste. But the army cannot clean up the pollutants that are already there, particularly those that have penetrated deep into the groundwater and soils.

Mining has led to many point sources of heavy-metal and other types of pollution across the world, which must be treated if we are to avoid severe consequences. The Rio Tinto in southwestern Spain is perhaps the world's most long-suffering river. It drains a watershed that has been mined for copper, silver and gold for 5000 years, and the 'red wine tint' (tinto) is the iron in solution caused by the exposure of sulphur during mining and the oxidisation of mine wastes, which have drained from large recent mines as well as from mines dating back to Roman times. It's a reminder that mines don't clean themselves up. Someone has to do it. Many old mines were dug before there was any thought of environmental remediation. It was only in the sixteenth century that pollution from mining and smelting was recognised and recorded as degrading the environment.[12] Governments are still wrestling with how to manage mining impacts globally, and in many countries mining companies operate with inadequate resources, financial provisions to fund closure and clean-ups. Many mines simply close prematurely or declare bankruptcy when the mines become marginal economically. Australia alone has 50,000 unremediated mine sites.[13] Yet the country has only been colonised by Europeans for 200 years. The number of unremediated mines worldwide must number in the millions, as must the kilometres of waterways polluted by them. The task of cleaning them up is almost beyond reckoning. Indeed, in 2012 the auditor-general of New South Wales said, 'derelict mines may represent the largest category of contamination liability for the state'.[14] Nobody knows how to deal with these problems at the scale required, so many mines are likely to continue to contaminate rivers and impact human health for decades or centuries—or until someone comes up with cost-effective solutions. The only saving grace in our current situation is that in the last

50 years, in some countries, our species is starting to acknowledge, document, legislate and take steps towards addressing our impacts.

The scale and complexity of the pollution problems outlined in this chapter put them in a different category from earlier pollution issues, such as that which killed the Thames, and they will require different approaches to cleaning them up. The job must begin soon, for the growing burden of polluted air, waters and soils represents an intolerable risk to human and planetary health.

CST technologies and seaweed farms could potentially play a large role in cleaning up this mess. Their roles are not restricted to the kinds of pollutants just discussed, but also include the excess carbon in the air and water that's causing climate change.

CHAPTER 6

The Big Clean-up

The history of Europe and the USA of the late twentieth century shows that it is possible to clean up rivers and other waters following decades—even centuries—of gross industrial pollution. It is also possible, at a small scale at least, to detoxify soils in a cost-effective manner. But something more will be needed to clean up, rapidly and cost effectively, the unprecedented diversity and scale of pollution facing us globally today. Some applications and technologies can help clean up pollution at the same time that they help grow food as well as draw CO_2 out of the atmosphere. Soils illustrates the interconnected nature of the various problems we face.

Soil pollution results from many sources, is varied in its nature, and is often hidden. Cleaning up cadmium pollution offers a valuable insight into how soil pollution as a whole can be tackled. Cadmium-contaminated soils have been successfully treated in Europe and the USA. The clean-up of the 2012 London Olympics site is one famous example. Located in the city's east end, in an old industrial area whose soils had been severely polluted for centuries by a cocktail of pollutants that reads like a guidebook to hazardous wastes, the site represented a formidable challenge. The solution settled on involved washing the soil kilogram by kilogram, then disposing of the condensed toxic fraction in a special landfill. This resulted in the removal of all major pollutants from the site—a complete remediation—which has allowed life, both human and wildlife, to thrive. Today, waterways and parklands have transformed the once-toxic dump into a vibrant and beautiful haven.

If east London's industrial wastelands can be cleaned up, there is no doubt that the knowledge exists to clean up China's soils. The problems, however, are cost and scale. It would take centuries to wash China's agricultural soils kilogram by kilogram, an undertaking that would probably bankrupt the nation. So other means must be found. One time-honoured method involves simply diluting the pollution until it is reduced to safe concentrations. This can be achieved by removing most of the soil and replacing it with clean soil, or diluting polluted soils by mixing them with clean soil. But when the problem affects nearly 20 per cent of all agricultural lands, the issues of disposal and transport are overwhelming. Alternatively, pollutants can be leached from the soil using acids. But the water and chemicals containing the pollutant then need to be cleaned themselves. Soil pollutants can also be bound into larger molecules, which makes them harder for crop plants such as rice to take up, but this method is most effective where the level of contamination is low. Using electricity to convey pollutants from the soil is also being tested. In the most extreme cases, such as with plutonium contamination, or where a very deadly pollutant is at high levels or very difficult to remove, the soil itself can be sacrificed by heating it in a kiln, or using in-situ electrical-arc processes until it is melted into glass or artificial rock, thereby neutralising the pollutant but also destroying the soil. Needless to say, this takes a lot of energy, and for many reasons is impractical at the scale required globally.

China is experimenting with all of these soil-cleaning options. Chinese researchers are also looking at ways of living with the pollution, including cultivating strains of rice that absorb less cadmium than those currently farmed. But the efficacy of many options is limited by the tragic reality that, in China, it is rare that just a single pollutant, such as cadmium, is present in the soils. More typically, a cocktail of heavy metals, pesticides and their residue, and breakdown products from chemical fertilisers, are present.[1]

Some researchers are optimistic that living things can, over time, affect a sort of clean-up. Plants that are not grown to be eaten, microbes or even earthworms can concentrate soil pollutants through bio-accumulation. The contaminated organisms can then be removed and disposed of. But imagine the cost in terms of lost production over years or decades, of allowing living things to slowly draw up the pollutants? And how would such a vast harvest of polluted plants (which would be voluminous), microbes or even worms be disposed of? One possibility is high-temperature incineration, and as some plants can accumulate four to six per cent of their dry weight as metal content, an economic case for such processes might be viable. Sadly, however, China's war on soil pollution is at a very early stage, and there are no immediately applicable large-scale easy fixes. The most promising approaches are in a purely experimental phase.[2]

There is one category of approach, however, that offers a middle road between the perfection of soil washing, and the pioneering possibilities outlined earlier, and that is the steam cleaning of soil. In fact, steam cleaning of soils has been going on for over a century, and it continues to be commonly applied in greenhouses to deal with infestations of nematodes, fungi or weeds.[3] Its one necessary prerequisite is cheap, clean heat to produce steam.

Steam can also be used to rid soils of contaminants on the broadacre scale.[4] Lower-temperature steam can be injected into soils in fields, so that contaminants are mobilised and concentrated for later treatment and/or disposal. At temperatures of up to 560°C, steam can more easily be used to physically remove the majority of pollutants from the soil. At higher temperatures still, steam can be used to break down many toxic molecules into their harmless component parts.

However it might be used, steam cleaning has the advantage of being a simple process using mobile devices that operate in situ, avoiding transport costs. In fact, a commercially available service using steam to remove mercury is already available in the USA. One drawback, however, is that the process is relatively expensive.[5]

But what if a cheap source of heat were available, and labour costs were kept low? Almost all of China receives sufficient solar radiation to make it suitable for CST technologies, particularly of the smaller, modular type. Because CST produces large volumes of high-quality steam, as well as distilled water and electricity, it could be used to decontaminate polluted soil as well as to provide power. Such plants could at the megawatt scale, for example, power small towns, provide clean drinking water, and remediate soils in the region. Whatever the current economic viability of such an approach, it is clear that China is going to require some outside-the-box solutions if it is to succeed at solving its most severe environmental problems.

There may also be a role for CST technologies in cleaning up oil-based pollutants in soil. It is normally difficult and energy-intensive to remove oil-based contaminants from soils, because the soils' water content hinders the normal oil extraction process. But dimethyl ether (DME) can be used to absorb oils from wet soils, then flash distillation can separate the DME and absorbed oil from the water. This process could prove far less costly and more effective.[6]

Providing clean water for human and agricultural use is one of humanity's most pressing problems, for not only are rivers, streams and lakes polluted, but so, increasingly, is groundwater. One measure, according to WWF, of the extent of the problem is the greywater footprint—the world's greywater footprint is the volume of water required to dilute to safe levels the pollutants released into waterways by humanity.[7] China's greywater footprint, for example, is 70 billion cubic metres per year. For many of the world's great rivers, there is simply not enough flow to supply their greywater footprint, so they remain polluted throughout their course.

The enormous problems faced by India in its efforts to clean up the Ganges illustrate just how great the task of cleaning up can be when there is insufficient water to dilute pollution to safe levels. Yet water polluted with human sewage is relatively easy to treat compared with that contaminated by industrial waste. Affluent countries treat virtually all water used by humans, including their sewage. But water-treatment plants are expensive, requiring chemicals, energy and ongoing maintenance in order to operate. The chance of providing India with such facilities seems remote, at least in the medium term. Moreover, the vast majority of such facilities depend, at least to some extent, on electricity generated by burning dirty fossil fuels such as coal and oil. And most conventional water-treatment facilities do not remove drugs, halogenated compounds and cyanides, antibiotics and hormone disruptors such as bisphenol A, among other pollutants.[8]

But what if we possessed a cheap and efficient way to strip all pollutants from drinking water? A way that did not involve burning fossil fuels? Many CST technologies use multi-stage flash distillation (a widely used process whereby water is converted to steam, and the heat is recovered for re-use by heat exchangers) to generate the steam required to generate electricity. Distilled water—water in its most pure form—is a byproduct of this process. Multi-stage flash distillation, incidentally, currently produces 60 per cent of the world's desalinated water. But tragically much of it is currently derived using energy generated by burning fossil fuels.

With their capacity to produce steam, which can be utilised to cleanse contaminated soils, along with their simultaneous ability to clean water, CST plants can be thought of as gigantic environmental clean-up machines. But of course they are more than that, for they can generate electricity (even when the sun is not shining) at the same time as they power greenhouses and heat dwellings. They may well be the multifaceted solution to Earth's myriad problems that we have been waiting so long for.

CST technology can be used to clean any water. In some regions of the world, groundwater is the principal water source. And in many places it is already polluted or highly vulnerable to pollution.[9] By cleaning groundwater and using the cleaned water for agriculture, CST can help remediate soils. In time, the clean water carries pollutants out of the soil. Plans are currently being laid to do just this in the 'triangle of death'. Discussions are underway to deploy three STEM units in the Campania region that will generate steam from polluted groundwater, which will then be fed into an existing waste combustion plant. The water from the polluted aquifers, once cleaned using flash distillation, will be used to help revive the region's damaged agriculture.[10]

As we have seen, clean, cheap heat generated by CST has huge potential to deal with two of humanity's most pressing pollution problems—contamination of our soils and waters. But what of the third pollution crisis—the excess of atmospheric carbon that is driving climate change? The supply of clean energy, and particularly its storage, are key elements in reducing the pollution stream. And CST technologies clearly have a vital role to play, but it seems possible that CST can do far more than that. The heat generated by CST can be used to break down CO_2 and convert its carbon into useful products. It can also be used to manufacture the perfect mechanism for capturing atmospheric methane—a greenhouse gas which over short time scales is 60 times more potent than CO_2 in terms of warming and is responsible for 11 per cent of global warming. The ability of CST to replace fossil fuels in electricity generation is well known. But the use of its heat to combat climate change is not.

In *Atmosphere of Hope*, I argued that the climate crisis has become so immense and dangerous that humanity has no choice but to pull carbon out of the atmosphere at the gigatonne scale if we wish to continue to live in a suitable climate. Humans are currently putting around 50 gigatonnes of CO_2 equivalent into the atmosphere. According to a new study, the need for the deployment of third-way technologies is even more urgent than I had thought.[11] The carbon budget framed by the IPCC argued that at current rates of emission, we have until at least 2030 before we will have emitted enough greenhouse gases to have committed ourselves to a future at least 2°C warmer than the preindustrial level. The new study, by contrast, argues that we have already put nearly enough greenhouse gases into the atmosphere to make 2°C of warming inevitable.[12] The difference is accounted for by the fact that the IPCC's carbon budget did not take account of methane or nitrous oxide, on the basis that their warming potential is offset by the dimming of sunlight caused by particulate pollution. This is correct, but the worst emitters of particulates—China and India—are moving urgently to reduce particulate pollution because it is such a serious health hazard. In a few years, the 'masking' effect of the particulates is likely to be much less than it is today. In addition, the IPCC assumes that Earth's carbon sinks on land and sea are holding steady. In reality they are weakening as Earth warms. By 2100, the new study warns, Earth's soils and ocean sequestration will weaken to the point that they draw 125 gigatonnes less carbon from the atmosphere than they would have if the warming had not occurred. Warming of the permafrost will have emitted 45 gigatonnes of CO_2 equivalent, a dying Amazon rainforest will have added 25 gigatonnes, the dying of the northern boreal forests another 20, and increased bacterial activity in the ocean a further 10. The extra carbon already coming from these sources as a result of current warming explains why CO_2 levels in the atmosphere continue to rise even though emissions have flatlined over the last three years.

If we are to avoid a catastrophe, humanity clearly needs to get onto an emergency footing to reduce emissions, for the current pollution stream remains staggeringly high. Its scale is perhaps best understood by examining what it would take, in terms of planting trees, to take just one-tenth of it out of the atmosphere on an annual basis. To do that, humanity would need to cover an area larger than Australia in forest, and to keep the trees growing vigorously for 50 years. There is clearly just not enough available land on the planet to offset our annual emissions from fossil-fuel burning by planting trees.

Atmosphere of Hope outlines what was known, as of mid-2015, of technologies that have the capacity to draw CO_2 out of the atmosphere at a scale that can make a difference to our future. The third-way technologies I described are mostly very new, and none are currently operating at anywhere near the scale required to draw even a single gigatonne of

CO_2 from the atmosphere. In the 12 months since I completed my research on that book, the rate of innovation in the sector has been truly astonishing. Not only have major advances been announced within existing technologies, but entire new fields of endeavour have opened up.

In August 2015, Professor Stuart Licht, a researcher in the Department of Chemistry at George Washington University in Washington DC, announced a novel electrochemical technique that allows the manufacture of carbon fibre directly from atmospheric CO_2. The breakthrough, which came after decades of patient research, was astonishing enough. But Professor Licht also claimed something truly attention-grabbing: he believes that his technique could produce carbon fibre at a lower cost than current methods of production. Carbon fibre is the lightest, strongest material currently available. Because it is expensive it is restricted to specialist uses such as aircraft and sporting equipment. Licht's process generates the fibres out of the air, and grows them on a substrate. If he is proved correct in his predictions of the cost of this new production method, the technique will have an enormous advantage over its competitors, and it may develop rapidly from its current laboratory status to an industrial scale.

Licht's discovery has profound implications. If carbon fibre becomes cost competitive with aluminium and steel, it could largely replace these metals. Aluminium manufacture is highly polluting, being responsible for potent greenhouse gases such as CF_4 (carbon tetrafluoride), which can last 50,000 years in the atmosphere,[13] while steel is responsible for 1.6 per cent of all human greenhouse-gas emissions.[14] If carbon fibre can eventually replace steel and aluminium, everything from motor vehicles to trains, trams and housing will become lighter and stronger, facilitating energy efficiency and the uptake of electric vehicles and new forms of construction.

Licht's process of manufacturing carbon fibre from atmospheric CO_2 involves a unique form of CST. Known as the Solar Thermal Electrochemical Photo (STEP) process, it works by harvesting energy from a wide spectrum of solar radiation. As a result, it can generate the high temperatures (up to 900°C) required to break up the CO_2 molecule, separating the carbon from the oxygen, and precipitating the carbon as a pure fibre.[15]

The process is highly efficient. Professor Licht and his team calculate that:

> given an area less than 10 per cent of the size of the Sahara Desert, the method could remove enough carbon dioxide to make global atmospheric levels return to preindustrial levels within 10 years, even if we keep emitting the greenhouse gas at a high rate during that period.[16]

This calculation is, of course, entirely theoretical. There is not a single commercial STEP plant in operation, so covering 10 per cent of the Sahara (an area of almost a million square kilometres) with them is a very distant prospect, if indeed it ever happens. Furthermore, there may be health impacts (carbon fibre being like fibreglass, which can be dangerous if it gets into our lungs). And it is hard to imagine humanity utilising the volume of carbon fibre that would ensue from such an exercise. Nonetheless, the vision is a powerful illustration of the potential scale at which CST technologies can operate to clean up our atmosphere, and so deal with the climate crisis.

Just after Professor Licht's team made its announcement, researchers in South Korea announced a second breakthrough of immense potential significance. This time it involved methane rather than CO_2, and the capacity of a humdrum waste product, when heat-treated, to capture it. The waste material is used coffee grounds, which were activated by soaking in sodium hydroxide, then heated to 700–900°C. The treated coffee grounds are such great absorbents of methane that the researchers didn't even need to wash and clean them before obtaining their stunning result.

The importance of this breakthrough can perhaps be best understood by looking at the process from end to end. A CST plant could easily provide most of the heat required to treat the waste coffee. The coffee could then be exposed to the air to allow it to capture methane, and once 'full' of the gas, the coffee grounds themselves would become a high quality fuel, part of which could be used to 'top-up' the heat from the CST plant, and part of which could be used elsewhere for heat and/or power. The methane, incidentally, is destroyed upon burning, though the less-potent CO_2 is created in the process). According to Christian Kemp, one of the study's authors from Pohang University of Science and Technology, the method has considerable advantages over every other methane-capture process:

> The waste material is free compared to all the metals and expensive organic chemicals needed in other processes—in my opinion this is a far easier way to go.[17]

It would be nice to think that each cup of coffee we drink is taking us a step closer to solving the climate crisis. Let's hope it will be. One indisputable fact is that high quality heat is essential to many carbon negative technologies. Indeed, the current global leader in direct air capture, the Canadian-based company Carbon Engineering, which hopes to commercially manufacture synthetic fuels with atmospheric carbon, requires temperatures of about 900°C for its process, and all direct-air-capture technologies require some kind of heat, none of which should be generated by the burning of fossil fuels.

There is another approach to carbon capture that promises to play a very large role in our future: the farming of seaweed and the high-quality protein-rich foodstuffs that can be grown in association with it. Seaweed farming may even offer a means of cleaning up one of Earth's most intractable problems—plastic pollution of the oceans.

Farming at sea is necessary to our future.

CHAPTER 7
The Future of Farming

On 21 June 2016, news media picked up on a very important story. Dr Challinor of the University of Leeds and his colleagues demonstrated that the effects of climate change across cropping land were now so rapid that current crop selection and breeding techniques were insufficient to allow food production to keep up. Unless things change immediately, within the next 30 years some food-production systems, such as that of maize in Africa, are likely to falter.[1]

The threat of climate change is not the only problem facing human cropping practices. Almost all are inefficient or wasteful at some level, often involving heavy use of artificial fertilisers (extracted with a high carbon footprint, from a hydrocarbon base in the case of nitrogen), soil loss, use of pesticides and herbicides that escape into the wider environment, and the destruction of biodiversity. Globally, many farmers are addressing these problems by adopting less-damaging practices including zero till and zero kill approaches to growing crops such as wheat. These practices protect biodiversity while maximising retention of soil carbon and minimising inputs of fossil fuels. Yet we are still very far from sustainable food production.

We humans are not the first species to develop agriculture. Ants and termites have been growing crops for tens of millions of years, and they have a great deal to teach us about sustainability. The agricultural systems of the leafcutter ants and the termites are vast, in some cases providing food for insect 'cities' with millions of inhabitants. Leafcutter-ant and termite agriculture have evolved completely independently of each other, as well as from human systems. Yet agriculture as practised by the ants and termites share several important features which helps explain their sustainable nature.

The most important characteristic of insect agriculture is that the ants and termites control as many variables as possible. They do this by establishing their farms underground (their main crops are fungi, which can grow in the dark), in specially built chambers inside their nests. In the chambers, growing conditions, including temperature and humidity, are kept close to ideal. Moreover, special kinds of antibiotics are judiciously applied, keeping pests to a minimum.

The closest we humans have ever come to such sustainable agriculture is inside our greenhouses. Until recently, greenhouses have required substantial inputs of fossil fuels and fresh water, and that makes them far less sustainable than any agricultural system that evolved among the insects. But a major breakthrough, made in the desert of South Australia in early 2016, has changed all of that. It means that humans can now grow crops without using a drop of freshwater, and with very little fossil-fuel, insecticide or herbicide use.

Sundrop Farms near Port Augusta in South Australia comprises just 20 hectares of greenhouses. It is located in the shadows of a rusting hulk of a coal-fired power plant, in some of the most unproductive desert in the world. The power plant was Alinta's Northern Power Plant, a 550-megawatt, inefficient and highly polluting facility. The coal that fed it contained so much uranium that the plant's smokestack became the single largest point source of radiation pollution in Australia. But the creaking dinosaur did have one asset: a saltwater intake on Gulf St Vincent, which served to cool the facility. When the Northern Power Plant closed in May 2016, 146 people lost their jobs. But by then the saltwater intake had been taken over by Sundrop Farms, and that facility had created jobs for 200 full-time employees, many of whom came directly from the Northern Power Plant.

One of the most astonishing things about Sundrop Farms is its productivity. Those few hectares of desert produce 10 per cent of Australia's truss tomato crop (tomatoes sold in clusters and still on the vine). It relies on a tower-type CST plant surrounded by about 3000 mirrors that focus sunlight on a receiver filled with saltwater. The water is vaporised by the heat, and the superheated steam turns a turbine, which generates all of the facility's electricity. Residual heat is used to maintain the temperature of the greenhouses at night and in winter. The condensed steam is pure fresh water which is used on the crops.

The tomatoes are grown hydroponically, on vines that can reach lengths of 10 metres. The water and nutrients are so precisely delivered that there is no runoff. The only waste is tomato vine clippings, which in future may be used in biomass combustion to replace the natural gas which is needed at times when the tower is not operating at full capacity, due to limited sunlight.

There are obvious risks to growing such a large proportion of any crop at a single facility. A disease, for example, could devastate the tomatoes and have a significant impact on food supply. But at Sundrop strict measures are taken to prevent this. For example, the system is compartmentalised. Teams of workers only ever enter one section of the establishment. This means that if disease is carried into a greenhouse, it will be restricted to that one section. The harsh desert environment outside the greenhouses also helps. Nobody nearby is growing tomatoes in their backyards for domestic use. Elsewhere, especially around major cities, such domestically grown tomatoes are a major source of diseases in commercial crops.

Because pathogens are so well contained by the physical measures taken and the outside environment, within the greenhouses pesticide and herbicide use is minimal. In addition, the conditions are so perfectly controlled that Sundrop Farms produces a very low percentage of less-than-perfect fruit (about one per cent, as opposed to three or more per cent elsewhere).

With reduced inputs of everything from fossil fuels to pesticides, and lower rejection rates, Sundrop

Farms' tomatoes are produced at a lower cost than less efficient systems, such as growing them in fields. The confidence the industry has in the system is underlined by the fact that one of Australia's largest supermarket chains has signed a 10-year agreement to take all of Sundrop's production.

There is considerable potential for Sundrop-style greenhouses to produce far more than tomatoes. In its experimental greenhouses, Sundrop's growers are trialling cucumbers and capsicums. And there is interest from North Africa and the Middle East in deploying the system. With the rollout of even more efficient CST technologies, Sundrop's approach may well form the template for a sizeable proportion of the world's future food production.

There are of course other methods of food production that are developing and which will have a role in feeding our increasingly crowded planet. One of the most strongly supported is the 'grow local' movement. The popularity of farmers markets, with their diverse offerings of heritage food types and organic produce that is often grown in close proximity to where they are sold, have strong community support and are increasing their market share. They will doubtless continue to supply one segment of the market. But none of those involved in this kind of food production would wish ill on the improvements made in mass production of food by the likes of Sundrop Farms.

There is a question around how the technology pioneered by Sundrop will develop as it is adopted. Australia already has a centralised form of food production, with supermarkets playing a large role so the opportunity is there for the uptake. In places like Africa this is less the case. When I asked people at Sundrop about the possibility that the system could be down-scaled so that it could be used at the village level in places like Africa, they stated that it might be possible. But that first, the system would need to be produced in multiplied quantities so that the cost of manufacture of its component parts fell.

The entire trajectory of human development has been shaped by the availability of freshwater. Our first civilisations developed along rivers whose annual flooding or irrigation brought life to crops. Our first cities grew up beside water sources. But as shown by Sundrop Farms, CST has the power to play a large role in turning that history on its head. The most productive land in future will be that with abundant sunlight and access to the sea. It is difficult to over-emphasise the importance of this breakthrough. It means that land which was previously considered to be almost completely useless is set to become some of the most productive farmland on Earth. The impoverished south could become the fruit-basket, if not the food basket, of the world.

CHAPTER 8

The Power of Kelp

Not only is the human population growing, but so is its demand for protein. As people's economic circumstances improve, they seek to eat more meat and high-status seafood. According to the World Resources Institute, by 2050 demand for meat will be up by 46 per cent on current levels in China, 72 per cent in the rest of Asia, 94 per cent in India and 29 per cent in sub-Saharan Africa.[1] The rising global demand for protein could result in a doubling of meat production by 2050.[2] From a sustainability perspective, this is potentially disastrous. Animals are higher on the food chain than plants, and generally the conversion rate for energy from plant to plant-eater is only 10 per cent. So, it takes 10 kilograms of plant matter to produce one kilogram of herbivorous animal. Putting it another way, if you feed a pig 10 grains of rice, you will get only one grain of rice back, in terms of energy, when you eat the pig.

The diversity of meat-production methods makes assessment of the global environmental impact of increased red-meat production highly complex. But the reality is that our increasing appetite for meat is being satisfied in a number of ways that are catastrophic for the environment. In rural parts of Africa and Asia, for example, an illegal trade in bush meat is helping drive some species to extinction. In the wealthiest nations, including the USA, feedlots which are wasteful of resources and can be highly polluting, produce most of the meat that is consumed. Red-meat production at the scale likely to be required in future cannot help but be land-intensive, polluting and wasteful of resources. In the best case, organic farms, which are careful to avoid pollution and toxic inputs, can produce meat with less environmental impact. But they are low yielding, their products are expensive, and therefore often seen as a luxury item. That is appropriate, because such meat reflects better the true cost of production, and it should underline the pattern of future meat use— that it be consumed less frequently, mostly only on special occasions—which should prevail in a more sustainable world. Beef eating, for example, once per week rather than every day, might also result in improved personal as well as planetary health. Yet this future vision of meat consumption leaves a big gap between the desires of the newly emerged middle classes, who have limited disposable income, and the cost of sustainable meat production.

Another stark warning that we must reduce meat production was issued in December 2016. Researchers studying methane concentration in the atmosphere have recently observed that it spiked in an alarming way. In the early 2000s, atmospheric methane concentration was increasing by just 0.5 parts per billion per year. But by 2016 it was increasing by 12.5 parts per billion. Just where all the extra methane is coming from is not clear, but the researchers commented: 'We think that agriculture is the number one contributor to the increase.'[3] Some of that agricultural rise is almost certainly coming from livestock. In light of these findings, humanity would be wise to begin reducing methane emissions from cattle through reducing beef consumption. That does not mean, however, that people must forgo the consumption of high-quality animal protein. It's possible that by 2050 new forms of aquaculture will be providing huge volumes of fish and shellfish, while also remediating environmental problems.

We should not imagine, however, that we can use the sea in the same destructive manner that we have used the land. The dire state of many wild-harvested marine resources points to the need to utterly change our attitude towards exploitation of the marine environment. The capacity of the world's fishing fleet is two-to-three-times larger than what can be supported sustainably, and a third of the world's fisheries, including all 10 of the world's largest fisheries by volume, are overexploited, while about half of all fisheries are fully exploited. It is predicted that, without change, stocks of all exploited species will collapse before 2050.[4]

In order to increase yields of marine resources, people are turning to aquaculture. Such activities have an ancient pedigree, going back at least as far as the ancient Roman praetor Caius Sergius Orata, who cultivated oysters in the Lucrine Lake—a coastal lagoon in the region of Baiae, in Italy, in the first century BCE.[5] But with the notable exceptions of oysters and seaweed, until recently, aquaculture accounted for a miniscule percentage of the seafood we consume. Over the last few decades that has changed, and the industry has grown spectacularly. Today, aquaculture accounts for about a third of all seafood consumed.[6]

Sadly, most aquaculture has a very mixed history in terms of sustainability. In enclosed waters, such as fjords and estuaries, nutrients from excess feed as well as the waste from the fish themselves have severely polluted waterways. Increased disease transmission along with 'genetic pollution' of wild stocks by domesticated strains remain major issues. But like land-based farming, aquaculture can be practised in ways that minimise impacts.

One form of sustainable aquaculture is called '3D Ocean Farming'. Bren Smith, an ex-industrial trawler man, operates a farm in Long Island Sound, near New Haven, Connecticut. Fish are not the focus of his new enterprise, but rather kelp and high-value shellfish. The seaweed and mussels grow on floating ropes, from which hang baskets filled with scallops and oysters. The technology allows for the production of about 40 tonnes of kelp and a million bivalves per hectare per year.[7] The kelp draw in so much CO_2 that they help de-acidify the water, providing an ideal environment for shell growth. The CO_2 is taken out of the water in much the same way that a land plant takes CO_2 out of the air. But because CO_2 has an acidifying effect on seawater, as the kelp absorb the CO_2 the water becomes less acid. And the kelp itself has some value as a feedstock in agriculture and various industrial purposes.

After starting his farm in 2011, Smit
cent of his crop twice—when the regi
hurricanes Irene and Sandy, but he persisted, and
now runs a profitable business.[8] The team at 3D
Ocean Farming believe so strongly in the environmental and economic benefits of their model that,
in order to help others establish similar operations,
they have established a not-for-profit called Green
Wave. Green Wave's vision is to create clusters of
kelp-and-shellfish farms utilising the entire water
column, which are strategically located near seafood
transporting or consumption hubs.

The general concepts embodied by 3D Ocean
Farming have long been practised in China, where
over 500 square kilometres of seaweed farms exist
in the Yellow Sea. The seaweed farms buffer the
ocean's growing acidity and provide ideal conditions
for the cultivation of a variety of shellfish. Despite
the huge expansion in aquaculture, and the experiences gained in the USA and China of integrating
kelp into sustainable marine farms, this farming
methodology is still at an early stage of development.

Yet it seems inevitable that a new generation of ocean farming will build on the experiences gained in these enterprises to develop a method of aquaculture with the potential not only to feed humanity, but to play a large role in solving one of our most dire issues—climate change.

Globally, around 12 million tonnes of seaweed is grown and harvested annually, about three-quarters of which comes from China. The current market value of the global crop is US$5–5.6 billion, of which $5 billion comes from sale for human consumption. Production, however, is expanding very rapidly.[9] Seaweeds can grow very fast—at rates more than 30 times those of land-based plants. Because they de-acidify seawater, making it easier for anything with a shell to grow, they are also the key to shellfish production. And by drawing CO_2 out of the ocean waters (thereby allowing the oceans to absorb more CO_2 from the atmosphere) they help fight climate change. The stupendous potential of seaweed farming as a tool to combat climate change was outlined in 2012 by the University of the South

Pacific's Dr Antoine De Ramon N'Yeurt and his team.[10] Their analysis reveals that if 9 per cent of the ocean were to be covered in seaweed farms, the farmed seaweed could produce 12 gigatonnes per year of biodigested methane which could be burned as a substitute for natural gas. The seaweed growth involved would capture 19 gigatonnes of CO_2. A further 34 gigatonnes per year of CO_2 could be taken from the atmosphere if the methane is burned to generate electricity and the CO_2 generated captured and stored. This, they say:

> could produce sufficient biomethane to replace all of today's needs in fossil-fuel energy, while removing 53 billion tonnes of CO_2 per year from the atmosphere...This amount of biomass could also increase sustainable fish production to potentially provide 200 kilograms per year, per person, for 10 billion people. Additional benefits are reduction in ocean acidification and increased ocean primary productivity and biodiversity.[11]

Nine per cent of the world's oceans is not a small area. It is equivalent to about four and a half times the area of Australia. But even at smaller scales, kelp farming has the potential to substantially lower atmospheric CO_2, and this realisation has had an energising impact on the research and commercial development of sustainable aquaculture. But, like CST technologies, kelp farming is not solely about reducing CO_2. In fact, it is being driven, from a commercial perspective, by sustainable production of high-quality protein.

One fundamental point about kelp farming is that N'Yeurt's vision cannot be fulfilled simply by scaling up current farming models. Existing farms are all located either onshore (Arcadia Seaplants Ltd in Nova Scotia, Canada, being the largest onshore facility) or in near-shore waters. This is because proximity to market reduces transport and other logistical costs, and the infrastructure requirements for near-shore seaweed farming are well understood. But near-shore environments are limited in extent, already face high usage for other purposes, and are vulnerable to ecosystem damage. Moreover, the issue of storing the carbon captured by seaweed in near-shore environments is a formidable challenge. If kelp farming is to reach its full potential, a model for mid-ocean farms is required.

The first person to think seriously about open-ocean farming of kelp appears to have been the American physicist Howard Wilcox. In 1968 he was working as a consultant to President Lyndon Johnson's Commission on Ocean Resources. He felt that open-ocean kelp farms might provide food, animal feeds, fertiliser and energy at a large scale.[12] While immensely challenging from a technical perspective, enough work has already been done to demonstrate that PV-powered mid-ocean kelp farming (PMKF) is feasible, and that while its development is expensive, it has considerable advantages over near-shore farms, particularly when it comes to storage of the captured CO_2.

There are thousands of species of seaweeds, but the organism most often considered for the large-scale capture of carbon offshore is the giant kelp *Macrocystis pyrifera*. Contrary to popular belief, giant kelp is not a plant, but rather is classified along with other algae in the phylum Heterokontophyta. Giant kelp is the largest of all algae, and one of the fastest-growing of all organisms. In ideal conditions it can grow 60 centimetres per day, and its fronds can reach lengths of up to 60 metres. Giant kelp occurs naturally on the Pacific coasts of the Americas, and in the waters of Australia, South Africa and New Zealand, where it forms dense 'forests'. Anyone who has walked an ocean beach adjacent to an offshore kelp forest will recognise its great leathery blades and floats which are washed ashore, often in great rafts. Giant kelp is, moreover, a keystone species—it supports thousands of other species as diverse as invertebrates, fish and even mammals such as the sea otter. As long ago as the mid-nineteenth century, Charles Darwin speculated that its marine forests rivalled the tropical rainforests in diversity—a view supported by decades of subsequent research. As the marine biologists David Schiel and Michael Foster say, 'Perhaps no other single species is so important in providing biogenic habitat in which thousands of species can live and interact.'[13]

Giant kelp has been harvested from the wild for over a century. It has even been grown commercially as a valuable source of soda ash (an ingredient used in glass and detergents), alginates (gel-like substances used for many things including thickening foods), iodine, potassium, vitamins and minerals. More recently, it has become of interest as a feedstock for farmed abalones and shrimps. Other seaweed species, however, are preferred as a food for humans.

The 1972 oil crisis saw researchers turn to giant kelp as a possible source of biofuel, though this interest lapsed as oil prices fell. More recently, the climate crisis has seen a growing interest in farming giant kelp to sequester atmospheric CO_2.

Despite its many favourable characteristics, growing giant kelp in any sort of farm—much less mid-ocean farms (PMKF)—is not straightforward. The species has a complex life cycle, with generations alternating between a microscopic sexual phase (in which the miniscule kelp organisms exist as separate sexes), and the much larger organism we recognise as mature giant kelp. China has taken the lead in giant kelp cultivation. In the Chinese method, the tiny sexual phase of the organism is cultivated in cooled greenhouses where conditions are tightly controlled, and which are located onshore, then the larger phase is transplanted onto long lines laid out in the sea, either on the surface or at shallow depth.[14] In the past, both China and the USA have made efforts to grow giant kelp far out to sea, suspended from floating frames. The Chinese discovered that the kelp, freed from the constraints of near-shore waters, grew to a large size. But operational challenges, principally surrounding the culture of the sexual phase of the organism in an offshore environment, along with problems concerning the maintenance of the floating structures, saw the Chinese projects shelved.[15]

In 1973, inspired by Wilcox's pioneering work and spurred by the oil crisis, the Californian Institute of Technology and the US Navy joined forces to conduct large-scale research into oceanic kelp farming. The research was to extend over 10 years and to cost several billion dollars. A series of farms was established, the first being a three-hectare array off San Clemente Island, California, which was an anchored structure floating in waters 125 metres deep. It and subsequent attempts fell victim to the sometimes extreme weather conditions seen along coastal California, and the farms were wrecked by storms. Despite the setbacks, the American Gas Association joined the program, ultimately contributing US$2 billion to it. A series of experimental structures yielded valuable experience about almost all aspects of kelp farming, before they too were closed as a result of design flaws and accidents.

The most long-lived of the farms built under the project was a shallow-water farm established in 1981 near Goleta, California. Experiments conducted there established that growth rates of giant kelp subject to the technologies expected to be used on deep-ocean farms were at least equivalent to those of naturally growing kelp. Other experiments proved that the kelp could be fed by pumping nutrient rich water from a depth of 350 metres to the surface, and that the kelp were able to reproduce on the farms—reproduction was a major stumbling block in the Chinese efforts.[16] These pioneering experiments came to an end when interest in using kelp for biofuels faltered, again as a result of dropping oil prices. Perhaps it's not surprising that farms anchored to the bottom in such a turbulent environment as coastal California would fall victim to storms. But back then, free-floating mobile structures were barely feasible.

Interest in utilising the open ocean for crop production has been revived, and the results of early work are being examined. Much has changed since the 1980s, when the last efforts to grow giant kelp at large scale in the open ocean were made. Among the most important are huge advances in computing, GPS technology, weather prediction, the availability of solar power and new materials such as carbon fibre. Together, these advances mean that today open-ocean kelp farming has a better chance of succeeding than ever before.

Given the prominent role that bad weather played

in the failure of earlier kelp farming, it's clear that location is an important factor. There are regions of the ocean where calm conditions prevail, such as the rainy intertropical convergence zones that circle the earth about 30 degrees north and south of the equator. Known in the age of sail as the 'doldrums', they are characterised by very still weather. Their precise locations and extents vary according to global atmospheric circulation patterns, and occasionally thunderstorms can disrupt the calm. But their generally tranquil conditions make them ideal for kelp farms. Given the likelihood that future, doldrums-based kelp farms would be mobile, and perhaps capable of submerging for a time to avoid storms, and given advances in weather prediction, it seems that weather damage to such farms could be minimised.

Much of the surface of the deep ocean is a biological desert. There is no life there because there are no nutrients. When it comes to kelp farming this is potentially beneficial, because it means that any farms operating there will not impact fragile ecosystems, or be impacted by them. But where would the nutrients to feed the kelp come from? It turns out that they are just a few hundred metres away. In 2010, researchers with Monterey Bay Aquarium Research Institute confirmed earlier studies showing that nitrates and other nutrients essential for algae to grow abound as close as 250 metres below the surface. The occasional algal bloom that is observed in what is otherwise a desert sea all but devoid of life occurs when deep currents bring those nutrients near enough to the surface for sunlight to reach them.[17]

The amount of energy required to pump water from a depth of about 300 metres to the surface is relatively trivial and could be easily supplied by solar-powered pumps. Indeed, solar technology is more than capable of providing the power for this as well as the other requirements of a mid-oceanic kelp farm, such as transport, refrigeration and lighting.

Giant kelp is not the only species suitable for stocking such farms. Bull kelp (*Durvillea*), which occurs at high latitude in the Southern Hemisphere, and vast expanses of floating sargassum weed

(*Sargassum*), which grows in the Sargasso Sea region of the Atlantic Ocean as well as elsewhere around the globe, offer further possibilities. Nor are the doldrums the only option in terms of location. The North Pacific garbage patch is a huge gyre that extends from 135° to 155° West, and 35° to 42° North. Most of the garbage consists of plastic particles suspended below the surface, and it seems possible that seaweed farming in this region could be linked with clean-up efforts, perhaps even using the plastic as fuel. And a clean-up is much needed because plastics from the gyre kill about a third of all albatross chicks born on Midway Atoll each year, as well as having a large impact on marine turtles and other marine life. Another unfortunate effect occurs as the plastics break down and release toxins including hormone disruptors that are consumed by microscopic creatures and jellyfish, then concentrated in fish, potentially arriving on our tables after bio-concentration.

How might such a clean-up operate? The plastic in the great North Pacific garbage patch is not, as you might imagine it, tightly packed, but diffuse, with about four, mostly small, pieces of plastic floating in every cubic metre of water. Interspersed with chemical sludge, it adds up to just 5.1 kilograms of waste per square kilometre of ocean surface.[18] Some work is already being done to deal with the problem. The Ocean Clean-up, founded by Dutchman Boyan Slat, focusses on inventing and developing technologies to deal with oceanic pollution.[19] It has already received over US $2.2 million through crowdfunding and sponsorship. Its vision is to use 'passive cleaning' to collect the plastics from ocean gyres. One-hundred-kilometre-long floating V-shaped barriers would be anchored to the sea floor, and the gyre currents themselves would concentrate the plastics in them. The project has won various awards, but remains in its earliest stages of development. There are plans to launch a pilot program using two-kilometre-long barriers off Japan. If the plastic waste can be captured, it could be burned or charred for energy, or compacted and encouraged to sink to the floor of the abyss, or perhaps be recycled. The entire process could be powered from bioenergy created from seaweed farming. Because, in most scenarios, there is no commercial product from such a process, it would have to be funded as a public good.

Not all kinds of blue-water kelp farms would have to float. The ocean has vast submarine plateaus to which farms could be anchored. The Saya de Malha Bank, northeast of Madagascar, is the largest submerged plateau in the world, with about 40,000 square kilometres of area lying at depths of between seven and 70 metres. When combined with Lansdowne Bank, a seamount located between Australia and New Caledonia, which has an area of about 21,000 square kilometres at depths of between 60 and 80 metres, over 60,000 square kilometres of shallow, mid-ocean area is useable. In such places, farms could be anchored and may be cheaper to build and maintain than those that float. Unlike farms located over deeper water, however, carbon-rich material (such as kelp by-product, or CO_2 itself) could not be sequestrated in the ocean depths, so alternatives would need to be found. One of the recurring problems for all such options, however, is likely to be cost. How could blue-water kelp and shellfish compete commercially with aquaculture located closer to cities? A carbon price might give them a competitive advantage, as perhaps could ecological or overall increased productivity benefits.

The importance of a carbon price if seaweed is to be used to sequester carbon has been emphasised in a recent research paper.[20] About 27.3 million tonnes of seaweed was grown globally in 2014. Only South Korea, responsible for 6 per cent of global production, has a blue-carbon program (effectively a carbon price) that includes seaweed. Demand for seaweed continues to outstrip supply. Norway, for example, is encouraging seaweed farming, and the area under cultivation tripled between 2014 and 2016. Seaweed use in biofuel and fertiliser production and as a feedstock for cattle to reduce methane emissions are all growing markets, which means that, in the absence of a carbon price, the amount of seaweed remaining to be disposed of in shallow marine sediments (around seaweed farms) is decreasing.

As more farms are developed, the gap between supply and demand is diminishing, and the price seaweed growers receive is declining by 1–2 per cent per year. This discourages new growers, but opportunities continue to emerge, including seaweed farms co-located with offshore wind farms, and farms positioned to reduce wave size, and thus slowing coastal erosion.[21]

What might a PMKF facility of the future look like? Dr Brian von Hertzen of the Climate Foundation has outlined one vision: a frame structure, most likely composed of a carbon polymer, up to a square kilometre in extent and sunk far enough below the surface (about 25 metres) to avoid being a shipping hazard. Planted with kelp, the frame would be interspersed with containers for shellfish and other kinds of fish as well. There would be no netting, but a kind of free-range aquaculture based on providing habitat to keep fish on location. Robotic removal of encrusting organisms would probably also be part of the facility. The marine permaculture would be designed to clip the bottom of the waves during heavy seas. Below it, a pipe reaching down to 200–500 metres would bring cool, nutrient-rich water to the frame, where it would be reticulated over the growing kelp. Dr Von Herzen's objective is to create what he calls 'permaculture arrays'—marine permaculture at a scale that will have an impact on the climate by growing kelp and bringing cooler ocean water to the surface. His vision also entails providing habitat for fish, generating food, feedstocks for animals, fertiliser and biofuels. He also hopes to help exploited fish populations rebound and to create jobs. 'Given the transformative effect that marine permaculture can have on the ocean, there is much reason for hope that permaculture arrays can play a major part in globally balancing carbon,' he says.

The addition of a floating platform supporting solar panels, facilities such as accommodation (if the farms are not fully automated), refrigeration and processing equipment tethered to the floating frame-work would enhance the efficiency and viability of the permaculture arrays, as well as a dock for ships carrying produce to market.

Given its phenomenal growth rate, the kelp could be cut on a 90-day rotation basis. It's possible that the only processing required would be the cutting of the kelp from the buoyancy devices and the disposal of the fronds overboard to sink. Once in the ocean depths, the carbon the kelp contains is essentially out of circulation and cannot return to the atmosphere. The deep waters of the central Pacific are exceptionally still. A friend who explores mid-ocean ridges in a submersible once told me about filleting a fish for dinner, then discovering the filleted remains the next morning, four kilometres down and directly below his ship. So it's likely that the seaweed fronds would sink, at least initially, though gases from decomposition may later cause some to rise if they are not consumed quickly. Alternatively, the seaweed could be converted to biochar to produce energy and the char pelletised and discarded overboard. Char, having a mineralised carbon structure, is likely to last well on the seafloor. Likewise, shells and any encrusting organisms could be sunk as a carbon store.

Once at the bottom of the sea three or more kilometres below, it's likely that raw kelp, and possibly even to some extent biochar, would be utilised as a food source by bottom-dwelling bacteria and larger organisms such as sea cucumbers. Provided that the decomposing material did not float, this would not matter, because once sunk below about one kilometre from the surface, the carbon in these materials would effectively be removed from the atmosphere for at least 1000 years. If present in large volumes, however, decomposing matter may reduce oxygen levels in the surrounding seawater.

Large volumes of kelp already reach the ocean floor. Storms in the North Atlantic may deliver enormous volumes of kelp—by some estimates as much as seven gigatonnes at a time—to the 1.8-kilometre-deep ocean floor off the Bahamian Shelf.[22] Submarine canyons may also convey large volumes at a more regular rate to the deep ocean floor. The Carmel Canyon, off California, for example, exports large volumes of giant kelp to the ocean depths, and 660 major submarine canyons have been documented worldwide, suggesting that canyons play a significant role in marine carbon transport.[23] These natural instances of large-scale sequestration of kelp in the deep ocean offer splendid opportunities to investigate the fate of kelp, and the carbon it contains, in the ocean. They should prepare us well in anticipating any negative or indeed positive impacts on the ocean deep of offshore kelp farming.

Only entrepreneurs with vision and deep pockets could make such mid-ocean kelp farming a reality. But of course where there are great rewards, there are also considerable risks. One obstacle potential entrepreneurs need not fear, however, is bureaucratic red tape, for much of the mid-oceans remain a global commons. If a global carbon price is ever introduced, the exercise of disposing of the carbon captured by the kelp would transform that part of the business from a small cost to a profit generator. Even without a carbon price, the opportunity to supply huge volumes of high-quality seafood at the same time as making a substantial impact on the climate crisis are considerable incentives for investment in seaweed farming.

CHAPTER 9

A Vision of the World in 2050

When I first began writing about climate change about 20 years ago, 2050 seemed a long way off. But now, with the mid-century just 33 years away, it feels like it's just around the corner. When I ask friends what life in 2050 might be like, most offer apocalyptic visions. I find it strange that even though most will still be alive in 2050, they are investing almost nothing in efforts to avert the apocalypse that they see taking shape.

Occasionally I'm accused of being a naïve optimist, but I think that history is on my side. A century ago there were more horses than horseless carriages almost everywhere. The great powers were blasting their young men into mincemeat by the hundreds of thousands, with no end in sight. The first aircraft flew above the fray, and tanks were shortly to join the carnage. But despite the fighting, the European empires, which had divided the world between them and which in some cases had lasted for centuries, appeared to be unshaken in their ascendency. In 1916, for example, there was not a single communist country on Earth.

How would you describe the world of 1950, with its jet aircraft, mechanisation, nuclear weapons and spread of communism, to someone living in 1917? Such is the gap driven by technological and social change over the intervening 33 years that 1950 would be unimaginable to them. Perhaps only the wildest writers of science fiction foresaw even a small part of it. Which is why I think that we must leave room in our imaginings for a fundamentally different and much better future.

In the 2050 of my imaginings, the human population has all but stabilised at around 9 billion, the majority of whom live in cities in Asia, Africa and South America. Driven by the demands of a new middle class, and enabled by new technologies, these cities are far cleaner, more efficient and liveable than those that exist today. A significant portion of humanity's food will be grown sustainably in greenhouses near the cities and with no input from fossil fuels or pesticides. Courtesy of CST technology, those located in desert areas near the sea will be especially productive, as these once-neglected regions will have become food production hotspots where employment and inexpensive food, energy and clean water abound. This shift will have gone some way towards reversing the inequality of today's north–south world. But it will have achieved far more than that. Rates of deforestation and soil erosion will have been halted or reversed as pressure for food production is taken off overused and exhausted tropical soils. As a result of cheap, clean energy, transport will be quiet, electrified, probably fully robotised, and almost entirely safe. The same CST plants that power and feed the cities will provide affordable freshwater through distillation, which will be far cleaner than existing supplies. And the horrific legacy of industrialisation, in the form of soil contamination will, once again courtesy of CST (at least in part), be a receding menace.

I believe that by 2050 our ever-sickening oceans will also have begun the long journey back to health. The plastic that so pollutes them today will be being sucked up and processed. Mid-ocean kelp farming will be supplying vast volumes of high-quality protein, in the form of shellfish and fish, to markets in distant cities. With pressure taken of overexploited fisheries, fish stocks, and thus marine ecosystems, will be recovering. The kelp will be absorbing so much CO_2 that the rate of ocean acidification is slowing. Locally, where kelp farms are being used to help restore ecosystem health, sensitive and hard-pressed ecosystems such as coral reefs will have a little breathing space.

We are so very close, yet so very far from my 2050. But wisdom, vision and determination can take us there.

Endnotes

INTRODUCTION

1 'Solar Power Passes 1% Global Threshold', *Clean Technica*, 12 June 2015, https://cleantechnica.com/2015/06/12/solar-power-passes-1-global-threshold/

2 McKie, Robin, 'Scientists Warn World Will Miss Key Climate Target', *Guardian*, 7 August 2016, https://www.theguardian.com/science/2016/aug/06/global-warming-target-miss-scientists-warn

3 WWF, *Living Planet Report 2014: Species and Spaces, People and Places*, Chapter 1: The State of the Planet, https://www.wwf.or.jp/activities/lib/lpr/WWF_LPR_2014.pdf

4 Randers, Jørgen, *2052: A Global Forecast for the Next Forty Years*, Chelsea Green Publishing, Vermont, USA, 2012, http://www.2052.info/book-2/

THE POPULATION BOMB

1 Ehrlich, Paul and Anne Ehrlich, *The Population Bomb*, Sierra Club/Ballantine Books, San Francisco, 1968.

2 Pinstrup-Andersen P., *Food Policy Report: Global Food Trends, Prospects for Future Security*, International Food Policy Research Institute, Washington DC, 1994.

3 Alexandratos, Nikos and Jelle Bruinsma, *World Agriculture Towards 2030/2050: The 2012 Revision*, ESA Working Paper No. 12–03, Food and Agriculture Organization of the United Nations, Rome, 2012, http://www.fao.org/docrep/016/ap106e/

ap106e.pdf

4 Ranganathan, Janet, 'The Global Food Challenge
  Explained in 18 Graphics', World Resources
  Institute, 2013, http://www.wri.org/blog/2013/12/
  global-food-challenge-explained-18-graphics

5 *Ibid.*

6 World Population clock, http://www.worldometers.info/
  world-population/

7 United Nations, *World Population Prospects: 2015 Revision*,
  United Nations Department of Economic and Social Affairs,
  2015, http://www.un.org/en/development/desa/population/
  events/other/10/index.shtml

8 United Nations, *Population 2030: Demographic Challenges
  and Opportunities for Sustainable Development Planning*,
  United Nations Department of Economic and Social Affairs,
  Population Division, New York, 2015, http://www.un.org/
  en/development/desa/population/publications/pdf/trends/
  Population2030.pdf

9 Index Mundi, http://www.indexmundi.com/g/r.aspx?v=31

10 Gallagher, James, 'Over 40s "Have More Babies" than Under
   20s', BBC News, 13 July 2016, http://www.bbc.com/news/
   health-36782323

11 Espenshade, T. J., *et al*, 'The Surprising Global
   Variation in Replacement Fertility', *Population Research
   and Policy Review* Vol. 22, 5, p 575, doi:10.1023/
   B:POPU.0000020882.29684.8e. https://en.wikipedia.org/
   wiki/Total_fertility_rate

12 Malthus, Thomas, *An Essay on the Principle of Population,
   as It Affects the Future Improvement of Society. with Remarks
   on the Speculations of Mr. Godwin, M. Condorcet and Other*

Writers, first published by J Johnson, London 1798, http://
www.esp.org/books/malthus/population/malthus.pdf

13 Lutz, Wolfgang, *et al* (eds), *World Population and Human
Capital in the Twenty-First Century*, Oxford University Press,
Oxford, 2014.

14 Randers, Jørgen, *2052: A Global Forecast for the Next Forty
Years*, Chelsea Green Publishing, Vermont, USA, 2012, http://
www.2052.info/book-2/

15 United Nations, *World Population Prospects: Key Findings and
Advanced Tables, 2015 Revision*, Department of Economic and
Social Affairs, New York, 2015, https://esa.un.org/unpd/wpp/
Publications/Files/Key_Findings_WPP_2015.pdf

16 Gerland, Patrick, *et al*, 'World Population Stabilization
Unlikely this Century', *Science*: 346: 234–37, 2014, http://
science.sciencemag.org/content/346/6206/234.

17 Family Planning 2020, *Momentum at the Midpoint 2015-2016*,
http://progress.familyplanning2020.org/

18 Ford, Liz, 'Contraceptive Rates in World's Poorest
Countries Leap by 30 Million Users in Four
Years' *Guardian*, 2 November 2016, https://www.
theguardian.com/global-development/2016/nov/01/
contraceptive-rates-poorest-countries-leap-by-30-million-
users-in-four-years-family-planning-2020-report

19 Li, Shuzhuo, 'Imbalanced Sex Ratio at Birth and
Comprehensive Intervention in China', 4th Asia Pacific
Conference on Sexual Health and Rights, Institute for
Population and Development Studies, China, and United
Nations Population Fund, 2007, https://www.unfpa.org/sites/
default/files/event-pdf/china.pdf

20 Fu, Peng, 'China's Sex Ratio at Birth Declines 4 Years in a

Row', *China News*, 5 March 2013. http://news.xinhuanet.com/
english/china/2013-03/05/c_132209268.htm

21 Jain, Mayank, 'Three Charts Show How Child Sex Ratio un
    India Has Dipped Further—But There Is a Silver Lining',
    Scroll.In, 4 January, 2016, http://scroll.in/article/801242/
    three-charts-show-how-child-sex-ratio-in-india-has-dipped-
    further-but-there-is-a-silver-lining

22 Meslé, France, *et al*, 'A Sharp Increase in Sex Ratio at Birth
    in the Caucasus. Why? How?' in Attané, Isabelle, and
    Guilmoto, Christope, *Watering the Neighbour's Garden: The
    Growing Demographic Female Deficit in Asia*, Committee
    for International Cooperation in National Research in
    Demography, Paris, 2007. Duthé, Géraldine, *et al*. (2011).
    'High Level of Sex Ratio at Birth in the Caucasus. A
    Persistent Phenomenon?', Princeton, 2007 http://epc2010.
    princeton.edu/papers/100423

THE STATE OF THE PLANET

1 *Living Planet Report*, WWF Global Footprint Network, 2014,
   http://www.footprintnetwork.org/en/index.php/GFN/page/
   living_planet_report2/

2 *Ibid.*

3 Ping, Xie, and Yiyu, Chen, *Biodiversity Problems in Freshwater
   Ecosystems in China: Impact of Human Activities and Loss of
   Biodiversity*, Institute of Hydrobiology, Wuhan, China, 2001.

4 Freyhof, Jörg, and Brooks, Emma, *European Red List of
   Freshwater Fishes*, Publications Office of the European Union,
   Luxemburg, 2011, http://www.iucn.org/sites/dev/files/
   import/dow nloads/rl_4_015.pdf

5 Galbraith, Heather, *et al*, 'The Secret Lives of Mussels:

America's Most Endangered Species', USGS April 4, 2013, https://www2.usgs.gov/blogs/features/usgs_top_story/the-secret-lives-of-mussels-americas-most-endangered-species/

6   'World Deforestation Slows Down as More Forests Are Better Managed', Food and Agriculture Organization of the United Nations, 7 September 2015, http://www.fao.org/news/story/en/item/326911/icode/

7   'Measuring the Daily Destruction of the World's Rainforests', *Scientific American*, 19 October 2009, http://www.scientific-american.com/article/earth-talks-daily-destruction/

8   Ceballos, Gerado, *et al*, 'Accelerated Modern Human-induced Species Losses: Entering the Sixth Mass Extinction', *Science Advances,* Vol. 1, 5, 19 Jun 2015, http://advances.sciencemag.org/content/1/5/e1400253

9   Duke, Norm, 'Large-scale Mangrove dieback 'unprecedented', TropWATER Centre, James Cook University, Townsville, 2016, https://research.jcu.edu.au/tropwater/news-and-events/large-scale-mangrove-dieback-unprecedented

10 Dean Miller, pers comms. Robinson, Joshua, 'Great Barrier Reef Bleaching for Unprecedented Second Year Running', *Guardian*, 10 March 2017, https://www.theguardian.com/environment/2017/mar/10/great-barrier-reef-coral-bleaching-worsens-as-scientists-fear-heatwaves-impact

11 Gynther, Ian, Waller, Natalie, & Leung, Luke K-P., 'Confirmation of the Extinction of the Bramble Cay Melomys *Melomys Rubicola* on Bramble Cay, Torres Strait: Results and Conclusions from a Comprehensive Survey in August–September 2014', Unpublished Report to the Department of Environment and Heritage Protection, Queensland Government, Brisbane, 2016, https://www.ehp.qld.gov.au/

wildlife/threatened-species/documents/bramble-cay-melo-mys-survey-report.pdf

12 Pike David A., *et al*, 'Nest Inundation from Sea-Level Rise Threatens Sea Turtle Population Viability', Royal Society Publishing, 2015, http://rsos.royalsocietypublishing.org/content/2/7/150127

ECLIPSE: THE TWILIGHT OF FOSSIL FUELS

1 Goering, Laurie, 'U.S. and China to Lead Push on Climate Change at G20 Summit', Thompson Reuters Foundation, 1 September 2016, news.trust.org/item/20160901153606-ps673/

2 Roberts, Dexter, 'China Trumpets Its Service Economy', *Bloomberg Businessweek*, 29 January 2016, https://www.bloomberg.com/news/articles/2016-01-28/china-trumpets-its-service-economy

3 *World Energy Outlook 2015*, International Energy Agency, Paris, 2015, https://www.iea.org/Textbase/npsum/WEO2015SUM.pdf

4 Deign, Jason, 'In 5 Years China Could Build More EV Chargers than the Rest of the World Combined', Greentech Media, 11 October 2016, https://www.greentechmedia.com/articles/read/china-could-build-more-ev-chargers-than-the-rest-of-the-world-combined

5 McCrone, A. and Mils, L., *Clean Energy Investment, By the Numbers, End of Year 2015*, Bloomberg New Energy Finance, 2016, http://www.bloomberg.com/company/clean-energy-investment/

6 'IEA Raises Its Five-Year Renewable Growth Forecast as 2015 Marks Record Year', International Energy Agency, 25 October 2016, https://www.iea.org/newsroom/news/2016/

october/iea-raises-its-five-year-renewable-growth-forecast-as-2015-marks-record-year.html

7   Shurtleff, Mike, 'The Continuing Exponential Growth
      of Solar PV Production and Installation', *Clean
      Technica*, 2014, http://cleantechnica.com/2014/07/22/
      exponential-growth-global-solar-pv-production-installation/

8   Owen, Michael, 'Warning of Energy Crisis to Hit the Nation',
      Australian, July 16, 2016.

9   Stiles, Jackson, 'Elon Musk Bets Millions on Fixing
      South Australia's Energy Problem in Just 100 Days', *New
      Daily*, 10 March 2017, http://thenewdaily.com.au/money/
      finance-news/2017/03/10/elon-musk-south-australia/

10   Lee, Jeong Min, 'Tidal Energy in Korea', *APEC Youth
      Scientist Journal*, Vol. 5, 2013, http://www.amgs.or.kr/New/
      common/journal/vol5/vol5_no.15.PDF

11   H. Lacey, pers. comm.

12   https://carnegiewave.com/projects/ceto-6-wavehub-uk/

13   Romitti, Yasmin, *The International Geothermal
      Market at a Glance*, Geothermal Energy Association,
      May 2015, http://geo-energy.org/reports/2015/
      Int'lMarketataGlanceMay2015Final5_14_15.pdf

14   Stock, Andrew, and Veena Sahajwalla, 'Powerful Potential:
      Battery Storage for Energy and Electric Cars', Climate
      Council of Australia, 20 October 2015, https://www.climate-
      council.org.au/batterystoragereport2015

15   Badwal, Sukhvinder, *et al*, 'Emerging Electrochemical
      Energy Conversion and Storage Technologies', CSIRO,
      Clayton South, 24 September 2014, http://journal.frontiersin.
      org/article/10.3389/fchem.2014.00079/full

16   Badwal, Sukhvinder, *et al*, 'Hydrogen Production Via Solid

Electrolytic Routes', *Wiley Interdisciplinary Reviews: Energy and Environment*, 15 August 2013, doi:10.1002/wene.50

17 Global Hydrogen Production, International Association for Hydrogen Energy, www.iahe.org

18 Barnard, Aenne, and Fenna Bleyl, 'Storing Renewably Generated Electricity', *Pictures of the Future*, 26 February 2016, https://www.siemens.com/innovation/en/home/pictures-of-the-future/energy-and-efficiency/smart-grids-and-energy-storage-energy-storage.html?WT.mc_id=Siemens+Pictures+of+the+Future+Newsletter+Raw+Materials+from+CO₂++Electrolysis+is+the+Key

19 *Electricity Monthly Update*, US Energy Information Administration, 24 June 2016, http://www.eia.gov/electricity/monthly/update/archive/june2016/

20 Hussain, Yadullah, 'Natural Gas Demand Growth Slows, Despite Low Gas Prices: IEA', *Financial Post*, 8 June 2016, http://business.financialpost.com/news/energy/global-natural-gas-demand-growth-slows-despite-low-gas-prices-iea?__lsa=607d-9fd4

21 Morris, Craig, 'Biomass—the Growth Is Over in Germany', *Energy Transition*, 1 July 2015, http://energytransition.de/2015/07/biomass-growth-is-over/

22 'Unique Community a Model for a Greener, Healthier Canada', *Natural Resources Canada*, 13 September 2007, http://web.archive.org/web/20071106023111/http://www.nrcan.gc.ca/media/newsreleases/2007/200784_e.htm)

THE UNIQUE POWER OF CONCENTRATED SUNLIGHT

1 https://en.wikipedia.org/wiki/List_of_solar_thermal_power_stations

2   Leitner, Arnold, 'Storage in Power Towers', *CST Today*, not dated, http://www.CSTtoday.com/pdf/storage.pdf

3   Bullis, Kevin, 'Cheap Solar Power—at Night', *MIT Technology Review*, 8 April, 2014, https://www.technologyreview.com/s/525296/cheap-solar-power-at-night/

4   Leitner, Arnold, 'Storage in Power Towers', CST Today, not dated, http://www.CSTtoday.com/pdf/storage.pdf Arnold Leitner is founder and former CEO of SkyFuel Inc.

5   Lanzarone, Giacomo, '"Project Archimede" Solar Energy Can Replace Oil', Studio Legale Avvocato Calogero Lanzarone Menfi, 2 July 2011, http://calogerolanzarone.blogspot.com.au/2011/07/carlo-rubbia-con-il-progetto-archimede.html

6   Leitner, Arnold, 'Storage in Power Towers', CSP Today, not dated, http://www.csptoday.com/pdf/storage.pdf

7   *Ibid.*

8   Sweet, Cassandra, 'High-Tech Solar Projects Fail to Deliver', *Wall Street Journal*, 12 June 2015, http://www.wsj.com/articles/high-tech-solar-projects-fail-to-deliver-1434138485. Danko, Pete, 'Ivanpah Solar Production Up 170% in 2015', *Breaking Energy*, 17 June 2015, http://breakingenergy.com/2015/06/17/ivanpah-solar-production-up-170-in-2015/

9   Kraemer, Susan, 'One Weird Trick Prevents Bird Deaths at Solar Towers', *Clean Technica*, 16 April 2015, http://cleantechnica.com/2015/04/16/one-weird-trick-prevents-bird-deaths-solar-towers/

10 Kagan, Rebecca A., *et al*, 'Avian Mortality at Solar Energy Facilities in Southern California: A Preliminary Analysis', *Palen Solar Power Project—Compliance*, National Fish and Wildlife Forensics Laboratory, Canada, 23 June 2014, http://

docketpublic.energy.ca.gov/PublicDocuments/09-AFC-07C/
TN202538_20140623T154647_Exh_3107_Kagan_et_al_2014.
pdf

11 Sweet, Cassandra, 'High-Tech Solar Projects Fail to Deliver',
Wall Street Journal, 12 June 2015, http://www.wsj.com/
articles/high-tech-solar-projects-fail-to-deliver-1434138485.

12 Handley, Kia, 'Fire Delays Forbes Solar Plant', ABC
News, 15 June 2016, http://www.abc.net.au/local/
stories/2015/06/15/4254876.htm

13 www.yedarnd.com/articles/heliofocus

SULLIED SOILS AND WATERS

1 *Punch*, 1855.

2 Hardach, Sophie, 'How the River Thames Was Brought Back
from the Dead', *BBC Earth*, 12 November 2015, http://www.
bbc.com/earth/story/20151111-how-the-river-thames-was-
brought-back-from-the-dead

3 *International Decade for Water Action 'Water for Life'
2005–2015*, United Nations Department of Economic and
Social Affairs, http://www.un.org/waterforlifedecade/quality.
shtml

4 Branigan, Tania, 'One Third of China's Yellow River "Unfit
for Drinking or Agriculture', *Guardian*, 25 November 2008,
https://www.theguardian.com/environment/2008/nov/25/
water-china

5 'Soil Contamination: A Severe Risk for the Environment and
Human Health', Global Soil Forum IAAS, Potsdam, 2014.

6 'Report: One fifth of China's Soil Contaminated',
BBC News, 18 April 2014, http://www.bbc.com/news/
world-asia-china-27076645

7 'Soil Contamination: A Severe Risk for the Environment and Human Health', Global Soil Forum IAAS, Potsdam, 2014.

8 Chatterjee, Pritha, 'WHO Clears Air: Delhi No Longer Most Polluted, that's Zabol in Iran', *Indian Express*, 13 May 2016, http://indianexpress.com/article/india/india-news-india/delhi-pollution-no-longer-most-polluted-but-4-other-cities-in-top-7-who-2797288/

9 Zutshi, Minna, 'Buddah Nullah: Stinking Reality of Ludhiana', *Tribune* (Punjab), 15 June 2015, http://www.tribuneindia.com/news/punjab/buddha-nullah-stinking-reality-of-ludhiana/93874.html

10 '"Triangle of Death": Italy Sends Army to Mafia Toxic Waste Dump', *RT*, 2 April 2014, https://www.rt.com/news/mafia-toxic-waste-army-937/

11 Hamzelou, Jessica, 'Italy's "Triangle of Death" Linked to Premature Ageing', *New Scientist*, 11 April 2012, https://www.newscientist.com/article/mg21428604-100-italys-triangle-of-death-linked-to-premature-ageing/

12 Georgius Agricola, *On the Nature of Metals (Minerals)*, 1556.

13 'What Should We Do with Australia's 50,000 Abandoned Mines?', *The Conversation*, 23 July 2014, http://theconversation.com/what-should-we-do-with-australias-50-000-abandoned-mines-18197

14 *Ibid.*

THE BIG CLEAN-UP

1 Guangwei, He, 'In China's Heartland, a Toxic Trail Leads from Factories to Fields to Food', *Yale Environment 360*, Yale School of Forestry & Environmental Studies, 7 July 2014, E360.yale.edu/feature/chinas_toxic_trail_leads_from_

factories_to_food/2784/

2 Zhitong, Yao, *et al*, (2012). 'Review on Remediation Technologies of Soil Contaminated by Heavy Metals', *Procedia Environmental Sciences*, Vol. 16, http://www.sciencedirect.com/science/article/pii/S1878029612006378

3 EPA, 'Steam as an Alternative to Methyl Bromide in Nursery Crops', in *Alternatives to Methyl Bromide Ten Case Studies: Soil, Commodity and Structural Use*, EPA, Washington DC, 1997.

4 David, Eva, 'Steam Injection for Soil and Aquifer Remediation', EPA Ground Water Issue, January 1998, https://www.epa.gov/sites/production/files/2015-06/documents/steaminj.pdf

5 Aresta, M. *et al*, 'Thermal Desorption of Polychlorobiphenyls from Contaminated Soils and their Hydrodechlorination Using Pd- and Rh-supported Catalysts', Chemosphere, January 2008, https://www.ncbi.nlm.nih.gov/pubmed/17850843

6 Kanda, Hideki, and Hisao Makino, 'Clean Up Process for Oil-polluted Materials by Using Liquefied DME', *Journal of Environment and Engineering*, Vol 4, No. 2, 14 September 2009, https://www.jstage.jst.go.jp/article/jee/4/2/4_2_356/_article

7 Mekonnen, Mesfin, and Arjen Hoekstra, 'Global Gray Water Footprint and Water Pollution Levels Related to Anthropogenic Nitrogen Loads to Fresh Water', *Environmental Science and Technology*, Vol. 49, No. 21, 6 October 2015.

8 'Removing Pollutants and Contaminants from Wastewater', Fraunhoffer IGB, 26 July 2013, http://www.igb.fraunhofer.de/en/press-media/press-releases/2013/removing-pollutants-and-contaminants-from-wastewater.html

9 Chilton, J., *et al*, 'Assessment of Groundwater Pollution Potential', WHO, Publications on Water Sanitation and Health, http://www.who.int/water_sanitation_health/publications/PGWsection3.pdf?ua=1

10 Professor Claudio Bertolli, pers. comm., 7 August 2016.

11 Will Steffen, pers. comm.

12 *Ibid.*

13 Harnisch, Jochen, *et al*, 'Primary Aluminium Production: Climate Policy, Emissions and Costs', October 2011, https://www.researchgate.net/publication/37594951_Primary_Aluminum_Production_Climate_Policy_Emissions_and_Costs

14 Birat, Jean-Pierre, (1999) 'CO$_2$ Emissions and the Steel Industry's Available Responses to the Greenhouse Effect', Presentation to the Seminar on Abatement of Greenhouse Gas Emissions in the Metallurgical & Materials Process Industry, San Diego, California, February–March, 1999, http://www.ulcos.org/en/docs/Ref16%20-%20Sdiego.pdf

15 Licht, Stuart *et al*, 'A New Solar Carbon Capture Process: Solar Thermal Electrochemical Photo (STEP) Carbon Capture', *Journal of Physical Chemistry*, Vol. 1, No. 15, 14 July 2010, http://pubs.acs.org/doi/abs/10.1021/jz100829s

16 Orcutt, Mike, 'Researcher Demonstrates How to Suck Carbon from the Air, Make Stuff from It', *MIT Technology Review*, 19 August 2015, https://www.technologyreview.com/s/540706/researcher-demonstrates-how-to-suck-carbon-from-the-air-make-stuff-from-it/

17 Mathewson, Samantha, 'Used Coffee Grounds Have a New Purpose', *Nature World News*, 2 September 2015, http://www.natureworldnews.com/articles/16435/20150902/

used-coffee-ground-new-purpose.htm

THE FUTURE OF FARMING

1   Challinor, A. J., *et al*, 'Current Warming Will Reduce Yields
    Unless Maize Breeding and Seed Selection Systems Adapt
    Immediately', *Nature Climate Change*, Vol. 6, 20 June 2016,
    http://www.nature.com/nclimate/journal/v6/n10/full/
    nclimate3061.html

THE POWER OF KELP

1   Ranganathan, Janet, '18 Infographics Illustrate
    the Global Food Challenge', *GreenBiz*, 3
    January 2014, https://www.greenbiz.com/
    blog/2014/01/03/18-graphics-illustrate-global-food-challenge
2   Alexandratos, Nikos, *et al*, *World Agriculture: Towards
    2030/2050*, interim report, Global Perspective Studies
    Unit, Food and Agriculture Organization of the United
    Nations, Rome, June 2006, http://www.fao.org/fileadmin/
    user_upload/esag/docs/Interim_report_AT2050web.pdf
3   Saunois, M. *et al*, (2016). 'The Growing Role of
    Methane in Anthropogenic Climate Change',
    Environmental Research Letters, Vol. 11, No. 12, IOP
    Science, 12 December 2016, http://iopscience.iop.org/
    article/10.1088/1748-9326/11/12/120207
4   'Unsustainable Fishing', WWF Global, http://wwf.
    panda.org/about_our_earth/blue_planet/problems/
    problems_fishing/
5   Günther, R. T., 'The Oyster Culture of the Ancient Romans',
    Journal of the Marine Biological Association of the United

Kingdom, Vol. 4, No. 4, Cambridge Core, 1 May 2009, https://www.cambridge.org/core/journals/journal-of-the-marine-biological-association-of-the-united-kingdom/article/oyster-culture-of-the-ancient-romans/EDB5C165BB46EDD3FA22C95C855325EB

6 'The Challenge of Sustainable Production', Food and Agriculture Organization of the United Nations, http://www.fao.org/focus/e/fisheries/challeng.htm

7 '3D Ocean Farming: the Least Deadliest Catch', http://greenwave.org/3d-ocean-farming/

8 'Bren Smith: Making Kelp Our New Hope', Climate Heroes, http://climateheroes.org/portfolio-item/bren-smith-making-kelp-ocean-farming-our-new-hope/

9 Benemann, John, 'History of US Department of Energy Macroalgae Projects—Major Conclusions', Washington DC, 11 February 2016, http://arpa-e.energy.gov/sites/default/files/Benemann%20ARPA-E%20MacroAlgae%20US%20DOE%20History%20Feb10%20FINAL.pdf

10 N'Yeurt, Antoine De Ramon, *et al*, (2012). 'Negative Carbon Via Ocean Afforestation', *Process Safety and Environmental Protection*, Vol. 90, November 2012, https://www.researchgate.net/publication/259892834_Negative_Carbon_Via_Ocean_Afforestation

11 *Ibid*.

12 Kelly, Maeve and Symon Dworjanyn, *The Potential of Marine Biomass for Anaerobic Biogas Production*. Marine Estate Research Report. Scottish Association for Marine Science, Oban, 2008, https://www.thecrownestate.co.uk/media/5765/marine_biomass_anaerobic_biogas.pdf

13 Schiel, David and Michael Foster, *The Biology and Ecology of*

Giant Kelp Forests. University of California Press, California, 2014.

14 Hoek, Christiaan, *et al*, *Algae: An introduction to phycology*. Cambridge University Press, Cambridge, 1995.

15 *Ibid*.

16 Kelly, Maeve and Symon Dworjanyn, *The Potential of Marine Biomass for Anaerobic Biogas Production*. Marine Estate Research Report. Scottish Association for Marine Science, Oban, 2008, https://www.thecrownestate.co.uk/media/5765/marine_biomass_anaerobic_biogas.pdf

17 Johnson, Kenneth, *et al*, 'Nitrate Supply from Deep to Near-Surface Waters of the North Pacific Subtropical Gyre' *Nature*, Vol. 465, 7300, 24 June 2010, http://www.nature.com/nature/journal/v465/n7301/full/nature09170.html

18 Moore, C. J. *et al*, (2001). 'A Comparison of Plastic and Plankton in the North Pacific Central Gyre', *Marine Pollution Bulletin*, Vol. 42, No. 12, http://www.sciencedirect.com/science/article/pii/S0025326X0100114X

19 Slat, Boyan, 'How the Oceans Can Clean Themselves', https://www.youtube.com/watch?v=ROW9F-c0kIQ.

20 Duarte, Carlos M. *et al*, 'Can Seaweed Farming Play a Role in Climate Change Mitigation and Adaptation?', *Frontiers in Marine Science*, 12 April 2017, http://journal.frontiersin.org/article/10.3389/fmars.2017.00100/full

21 *Ibid*.

22 Dierssen, H.M., *et al*, 'Potential Export of Unattached Benthic Macroalgae to the Deep Sea through Wind-Driven Langmuir Circulation', *Geophysical Research Letters*, Vol. 36, 18 February 2009, http://onlinelibrary.wiley.com/doi/10.1029/2008GL036188/pdf

23 Krause-Jansen, Dorte, and Carlos Duarte, 'Substantial Role of Macroalgae in Marine Carbon Sequestration', *Nature Geoscience*, 12 September 2016, http://www.nature.com/ngeo/journal/v9/n10/ngeo2790/metrics/news

Acknowledgments

I would like to thank Brian van Hertzen, Claudio Bertolli, Harley Lacy and Michael Heyward for reading this book in draft and providing invaluable comments. As always, Jane Pearson proved to be a brilliant editor.